PSYCHIATRY
AND
PASTORAL
CARE

SUCCESSFUL PASTORAL COUNSELING SERIES

PSYCHIATRY AND PASTORAL CARE

EDGAR DRAPER, M.D.

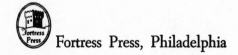

Fortress Press, Philadelphia

First published in the SUCCESSFUL PASTORAL
COUNSELING SERIES, edited by Russell L. Dicks, this
edition is reprinted by arrangement with Prentice-Hall, Inc.,
Englewood Cliffs, New Jersey

First FORTRESS PRESS Paperback Edition 1968

Library of Congress Catalog Number 65-23861

5715E67   *Printed in U.S.A.*   1-5013

INTRODUCTION

This series of books represents the most comprehensive publishing effort ever made in the field of pastoral care. These books could not have been published twenty-five years ago or probably even ten, for the material was not then available. In the past, single books have been available covering different phases of the task. Now we are bringing the subjects together in a single series. Here we present a library of pastoral care covering the major topics and problems that most pastors will encounter in their ministry. Fortunately, not all of these problems need be faced every week or even every month. But, when they are, the minister wants help and he wants it immediately.

These books are prepared for the nonspecialized minister serving the local church, where he is the most accessible professional person in the community. It is a well-accepted fact that more people turn to clergy when in trouble than to all other professional people. Therefore, the pastor must not fail them.

Russell L. Dicks
General Editor

PREFACE

It has become popular in our day to call psychiatrists all kinds of names. These loving appellations include "wig-picker," "head shrinker," "nut cracker," "brain buster," "couch artist," "witch doctor," "skull doctor," "nerve doctor" and may I add, "nervous doctor." Whatever natural resources contribute to my anxiety, the task before me makes this particular psychiatrist nervous! As the only representative of my specialty in this series, the editor, publishers, and reader may well expect this volume to provide *the* answers to the problems that are shared by the pastorate and psychiatry, as well as the ones that we make for each other. This kind of expectation may even be augmented by my bilateral training for the ministry and medicine. But as psychiatrists often do, let me dash at the outset omniscient hopes of the reader and not promise answers to all his questions nor solutions to the multiple problems that face us in psychiatry and pastoral care. If, however, some of the problems are explored and "interpretations" of merit hit the target, perhaps there will be some who feel this expedition has been worthwhile.

Sigmund Freud's discoveries stand alone and command respect in their revelation of new truths in the murky workings of man's mind. My debt to him and my teachers for their scientific contribution cannot be repaid. Many of the ideas expressed in this book are stimulated by or are translations of his contributions. The science of this book I owe to him. Its philosophy I must take as my own personal responsibility.

A glimpse of Freud's profundity as well as his own interest in matters religious can be grasped in this excerpt: "Critics persist in

7

ascribing as 'deeply religious' anyone who admits to a sense of man's insignificance or impotence in the face of the universe, although what constitutes the essence of the religious attitude is not this feeling but only the next step after it, the reaction to it which seeks a remedy for it." While it is this second step he calls the essence of a true religious attitude, he designates and identifies with "the man who goes no further but humbly acquiesces" as irreligious.[1] Although Freud has been indicted as an enemy of religion, Erich Fromm[2] questions this accusation and places Freud as an ally to religion's highest aspirations! Indeed, Fromm presents a convincing case that of the two men, Freud and Carl Jung (the so-called psychological apologist for religion), the former must be considered as more religious from Fromm's standpoint. Fromm develops his ideas about what is "truly" religious about religion and finds in the generous analysis of Freud's works that the Austrian stands closer to the spirit of religion than the Swiss doctor.

Whatever was Freud's "real" position on religion, we can perhaps adopt something of his courageous spirit. We humbly acknowledge the overwhelming problems facing us in the delimited universe of pastoral care. We are forced to screw up our courage and forge ahead looking for remedies in this real world which may present themselves after we sift away some of the vagueness so rampant in the relationship between psychiatrists and pastors.

Although my debt is multiple to those who contributed to the evolution of this work, special thanks are due, first, to my family for their patience, and my secretaries for their industry. Secondly, I want to indicate my appreciation to the Lilly Foundation and the National Institute of Mental Health. These perennially enlightened benefactors generously provided funds for the Kokomo-LaGrange Projects that allowed Rev. Granger Westberg and me opportunity to design, execute, and learn together from a truly experimental teaching venture for ministers. I would like to acknowledge the kind

[1] Sigmund Freud, *The Future of an Illusion, The Standard Edition of the Complete Psychological Works of Sigmund Freud,* Vol. XXI, Hogarth Press, London, 1961, p. 32.

[2] Erich Fromm, *Psychoanalysis and Religion,* Yale University Press, New Haven, 1950.

consent of Basic Books, Inc., and the University of Chicago Press to use excerpts from their publications. My gratitude is expressed to Chaplain Carl Nighswonger, Rev. Carroll Wise, Dr. Harry Trosman, and Dr. Henry Coppolillo for the valuable assistance of each in keeping my perspectives of both the pastor's and the psychiatrist's point of view close to focus. I had originally included Rev. Russell Dicks with these men because of his expert editorial suggestions for this volume. However, his untimely death and his fruitful life before it requires special salute from all of us who treasure the value of a studied ministry.

CONTENTS

CHAPTER ONE

PASTORS, PSYCHIATRISTS, and PSYCHES

When it comes to casting out devils, controversy over qualifications for the healer is as impassioned today as it was in ancient Biblical days. Who should lay claim to the mending of the spirit of man? St. John complained to Jesus, " 'Master, we saw one casting out devils in thy name and he followeth not us: and we forbade him, because he followeth not us.' But Jesus said, 'Forbid him not, for he that is not against us is on our part.' " (Mark 9:38–40) Though the spirit of his response may offer guidance, Jesus' simple answer offers no easy solution in our complicated world for the treatment of man's mind.

A contest in bewilderment over "Who's Who?" held between clergymen and psychiatrists might well result in a stand-off with each claiming victory as most confused. But pastors and psychiatrists have a right to be confused about each other. One could almost say, "That's normal!" It is as difficult for the pastor to find a psychiatrist who speaks his language as it is for the latter to find a minister who savvys what he does with patients. If the psychiatrist thinks he has a unique problem with the clergy's multiple denominations, schools of theology, church polity, diversions of practice and rainbow of pastoral qualifications (not to mention counseling qualifications), the pastor can quickly witness to an equally confusing array that he faces in the army of medical psychology. For example, the pastor might find a qualified psychotherapist in the professional garb of a physician (with some psychiatric training); a psychiatrist (an M.D. with three years of specialty training); a psychoanalyst (an M.D. with residency and psychoanalytic training); or a psychologist, a social worker, or a lay analyst (a non-M.D. with psychoanalytic training).

More confusing, he might search in vain in the ranks of some schools of psychiatry (so-called "organically oriented") for a competent psychotherapist and in vain in other schools of psychiatry ("psychoanalytically oriented") for a psychiatrist who prescribes medicine or gives shock treatment. One major advantage in this huge identification problem that rests with a clergyman, however, is that if he takes the trouble, he can find out the gross credentials, qualifications, experience, and aptitudes of a psychiatrist in the *Directory of Medical Specialists*[1] or through his requests of a local medical center, society or general physician.

Rather than belabor this staggering problem of identification, which I suspect has confronted readers in one form or another, I would prefer to move on to still more provocative problems. Even if we were to limit ourselves to the relationship of the "modern liberal pastor" with the "psychodynamically oriented psychiatrist" the problems of responsibility, philosophical orientation, and practical cooperation remain staggering. I believe that the difficulty in such relationships can be classified in a manner that may help us understand why they are characterized by heat more than light.

First of all, problems in the practical aspects of the psychiatrist-pastor relationship are worthy of mention as generators of tremendous friction. It has been striking to me, having worked on both sides of the fence, how frequently a member of one of the professions feels he has to "pick up the pieces" of a parishioner or a patient maligned by his professional "antagonist." Common complaints of the psychiatrist include, "Why don't ministers stick with religion and pray with their parishioners instead of giving them therapy?" Or, "That guy ought to be kept out of the hospital all together. He only stirs up my patients and never asks whether he should visit or not." Or, "He pretends to know psychology, but he does everything psychologically wrong." Or, "What business is it of his how I choose to treat my patients or how long?"

The minister's protests include, "The psychiatrist tells me nothing. I don't know what's going on with my parishioner." Or, "Why refer

[1] *Marquis Who's Who, Incorporated,* Volume XI, 1963–64, Marquis Publications, Chicago, Illinois.

someone to him? He'll just destroy their religion." Or, "When I asked him how I could help he said, 'Forget it.'" Or, "My parishioner isn't crazy at all. I don't see why I should encourage her to see a psychiatrist. He's liable to really mix her up." There is hardly a pastor or psychiatrist who could not add his own epithet, tale of woe, gross misunderstanding or question regarding the behavior observed in "that other profession." Unfortunately, certain members of both professions at times make their irresponsibility obviously clear and deserve the admonition not only of their inter-professional colleagues, but of their own as well. Some of the critical questions pastors might ask of psychiatrists, for instance, might be raised with equal force by members of their own specialty or their medical colleagues.

Problems at the practical level often stem from unilateral or bilateral ignorance. Some emanate from personality clashes or vicissitudes of character makeup. Some erupt because of the impersonal no-man's land that keeps "interaction" at the level of a silent, cold war wherein misunderstandings persist. In my own experience I have routinely found in both professions that their competent members behave responsibly toward each other. I have not found pastors (except characterologically irresponsible ones) using their training, station, or psychological insights inappropriately or in an inflammatory manner. I have yet to encounter a psychiatrist of merit who was unwilling to communicate with a rabbi or pastor when a patient's welfare rested on a collaborative understanding, or who was ready to write off the beliefs of a patient as meaningless prattle. With the promise of treatment in later sections of a few of the thorny practical issues that prick pastor-psychiatrist relationships, we turn to philosophical and theoretical concerns that hinder interest in collaboration between menders of man's mind and healers of his soul.

The "final death blow" to religion struck by science has been dealt many times. Discoveries in the universe from the days of Harvey, Copernicus, and Darwin to the Dead Sea Scrolls of our day have conflicted with established theologies. It may be possible to trace religion's history by its responses to various scientific discoveries, its reformers, heretics, and revolutionists. The Church has shown not only remarkable ability to roll with the punches that few professional boxers possess, it has been expert at counter-punching. Because the Church lives in the scientific age, it knows the ways of science and assimilates its contributions and methods, its rules and shortcomings. As scientific inquiry has permeated our world, religion has quickly adapted scientific findings to its own service—and why not! Advances in structural engineering have been put to use through beautifying modern church architecture; sociological studies help determine locations for new churches and the abandonment of dying ones; statistical analyses can measure effectiveness of church programs or religious educational techniques. And we hear a newly coined phrase built into some modern preachers' sermons, "Psychiatrists tell us . . ."

This phrase catches us up short as it does any psychiatrist who might be worshipping in such a congregation. Whatever follows those three words, the listener can be sure of only one thing—that the authority of psychiatrists will bear out the preacher's point! Our concern here is not a homiletic one. Rather, the phrase offers us a concrete handle with which to grab hold of a basic issue that troubles both the psychiatrist and pastor. On each side of the fence, these two professional groups do not mind—they, in fact, feel complimented— when their fields are appreciated in their contribution. But when psychiatrists view the Church as an instrument of mental health, or pastors ingest psychiatry's findings, each to their own purposes, we run into the problem of conflictual vested interests. It is being used that chafes. It is true that religion has been accustomed to attack and capable of rolling with punches and even counter-punching since long before the psychological revolution ushered in by Sigmund Freud. *But how does religion face and respond to psychological study?*

A characteristic of scientific inquiry is that it carries little respect for the vested interests of its object of study whether the object be the survival mechanisms of destructive organisms, the mitotic activities of cancerous cells, the mores of a culture, or the psychologically self-preservative and evangelistic interests of organized religion. Freud's findings were revolutionary enough for his Victorian world, but his specific treatment of religion, especially in "The Future of an Illusion" and "Civilization and Its Discontents" was, and is, to many religionists inflammatory as the devil himself. One of Freud's finest personal characteristics was his courageous, unswerving loyalty to the search for psychological truth. He believed his exposure of religion to psychoanalytic investigation to be completely consistent with the doctrine "The truth shall set ye free." Controversy's heat found new fuel not simply in his devotion to the pursuit of truth, whatever its consequences in the psychological realm, but in his conviction that his findings were a service to man—a goal shared by religion's aspirations!

Let me quickly reassure the reader that our intent here is not to enter the arena of scholarly assessment of Freud's impact on religion. Nor can we appropriately here luxuriate in an analysis of his philosophy. Rather, as a psychiatrist schooled in Freud's psychology and a person exposed to philosophical discipline, I wish to present my own impressions which I feel are consistent with the intent of this book as it addresses itself to problems confronting psychiatry and pastoral care. Besides the contribution of my dual training and influences of my own personal life experience, the observations I would like to make in this area are based on my work with patients, my collaboration with pastors, my activities in religious and mental health groups; but they most impressively stem from observations gleaned from a particular psychiatric study of religious meanings and its impact on colleagues in the field of both religion and psychiatry. The variety of reactions of various groups and individuals to this study (which is to be discussed later in summary fashion) tempted me to begin a paper with the title: "Climate for the Scientific Psychological Investigation of Religion: Cannibalism, Incest, and Murder!"

When we move away from the broad telescopic views of Freud's impact on our culture to the narrowed, almost microscopic fields of our interest here—namely, pastoral psychology, religion and personality, psychoanalysis, schools of psychiatry and psychotherapy—the "obvious" distinctions between philosophy and science become as vague as the outline of a pencil's mark examined under a high power lens. We find theologians who behave and believe as agnostic scientists as easily as we can observe psychoanalysts who behave and believe more like theologians. What is interesting in this respect is that with equal ease the agnostic theologian, abandoning the application of the discipline of philosophical objectivity, continues to consider himself a "believer" and the psychoanalytic philosopher, a "scientist!" While such a psychoanalytic philosopher may view religion as psychological sickness, his counterpart theologian labels psychoanalysis as a "Church of the Unconscious."[2]

Although there may be tepid or even comfortable approaches in the scientific study of religion, the psychoanalytic or psychodynamic studies of religion cannot be so. Because the psychological study of religion touches on the spirit of man, looks at the soul and brings its own theoretical framework to bear on the nature of man, it should be no surprise that steam and smoke are inevitable. Sociological studies which might reveal that women are better church-goers than men are far less provocative than a psychiatric study involving, for example, the case report of a woman who attends church because of her unconscious erotic interest in the pastor which confines her "worship" to an earth-bound "Electra-complex."

So, systems of belief and methods of research may be mutually provocative—but cannibalistic, incestuous, and murderous? Freud considered the inclination to commit these particular crimes against man and civilization to be born afresh with every child.[3] He considered only cannibalism to be universally proscribed and completely surmounted as a human action (though not as a human urge). Perhaps it is not unrelated that we find sublimative expressions and prohibitions of this particular instinctual wish so prominently on display between adherents of philosophical systems. Freud anticipated a willingness of others to engulf the findings or instrument of psychoanalysis. "If the application of the psychoanalytic method makes it possible to find a new instrument against the truths of religion, *tant pis* for religion; but defenders of religion will, by the same right, make use of psychoanalysis in order to give full value to the affective significance of religious doctrines."[4] Cannibalistically, religion has

[2] David C. McClelland, "Religious Overtones in Psychoanalysis," *Princeton Seminary Bulletin*, Vol. LII, January, 1959, p. 25.
[3] Freud, *op. cit.*, p. 10.
[4] *Ibid.*, p. 37.

been ready to devour, consume, subsume and assimilate other systems of belief or scientific findings. Erasing traces of contra-dogmatic characteristics began as early as the Jahweh, Elohim, and Priestly redactions of the Old Testament. At times certain religionists' attitudes toward anything unorthodox under the sun resembles that of the only two survivors of an atomic blast who meet each other amidst the rubble with the greeting, "Well, what's new?"

It is not too difficult to find some adherents of Freud with as ready an inclination to assign genuinely new findings or perspectives to Freud as though he had omnipotently predicted them. Psychoanalytic papers, often begin with a quotation from somewhere in Freud's vast writings, reminiscent of a sermon's biblical text which lends authority and "orthodoxy" for what is to follow.

But if there is a willingness of some to incorporate new findings into old Freudian metapsychology, it is insultingly sacrilegious to a Freudian devotee to tell him "all this business of the workings of the unconscious mind was anticipated way back there before Freud. Even Jesus knew about the unconscious. Didn't he condemn the hypocrisy of scribes and Pharisees who were like whited sepulchers, beautiful on the outside (conscious activity) but full of dead men's bones on the inside (their id and unconscious mind)?" Such a comment holds no less a negative charge than to inform a rabbi that the prophets are more Christian than Jewish because they foretold the coming of Christ. Psychoanalytic philosophers with peculiar approaches to "applied psychoanalysis" have been close to evangelistic fervor in their eagerness to swallow up man's behavior, history, art, theater, literature, philosophy, culture, and religion under the aegis of an "analytic" world view which at times seems ready to explain all.[5] Thus, while some Freudian zealots build metapsychological systems —encompassing the nature of man, his world and value systems—and dissect the realm of philosophy with clinical tools, theologians blithely ingest clinical concepts into incorporative systems of their own.

[5] For a sound analysis of the principles of applied psychoanalysis, see Heinz Kohut's article "Beyond the Bounds of the Basic Rule, Recent Contributions to Applied Psychoanalysis," *Journal of the American Psychoanalytic Association*, Volume VIII (1960), pp. 567–586.

This cannibalistic tendency is not a problem with theologians and metapsychologists alone. Schools of psychology like to chew on each other, too. As contributive a writer as Rollo May, an advocate of existential psychology, subtly succumbs to this man-eating sublimation. He states, "Any therapist is existential to the extent that, with all his technical training and his knowledge of transference and dynamisms, he is still able to relate to the patient as 'one existence communicating with another' to use Binswanger's phrase. In my own experience, Frieda Fromm-Reichmann particularly had this power in a given therapeutic hour . . . Erich Fromm, for another example, not only emphasizes presence in a way similar to Jasper, but makes it a central point in his teaching of psychoanalysis. Carl Rogers is an illustration of one who, never having had, so far as I know, direct contact with existential therapists as such has written a very existential document in his *Apologia pro Vita Sua* as a therapist."[6] This excerpt of May's tells us that to some extent all therapists are existential whether they realize it or not. He claims Frieda Fromm-Reichmann, Erich Fromm, and Carl Rogers as existentialists who simply have not adopted the name.

But if there are mutually digestive interests by adherents within the camps of religion and psychiatry, there have been *incestuous* ones as well. There are "ecumaniacs" and matchmakers eager to unite religion and psychiatry in a union no more legitimate than Oedipus'. These zealous reconciliators may find "no basic differences but a direct continuity from psychiatry or psychoanalysis to religion. Think only of what we share together and could do as a team for mental-spiritual good. Are not our goals identical and any differences superficial when we look at the individual?" One can hear such a position overtly expressed by evangelists for "religious mental health" or "mentally healthy religion."

Psychiatry, so recently emancipated from neurology, lives in the divided house of the organically and psychodynamically oriented schools. The latter group yearns for still greater independence from medicine than it has. But wary of a "spiritual identification," it

---

[6] Rollo May, *Existence, a New Dimension in Psychiatry and Psychology* (New York: Basic Books, Inc., Publishers, 1958), p. 81.

pleads with its constituents that they remember that they are first of all physicians. Because psychiatric investigations are often viewed as "soft" science by research colleagues, psychiatrists are at times supersensitive to comparison with shamans, witch doctors, or clergy. (They may admit though that their children are reviewed like a new brand of "PK's" [Preachers' Kids] by laymen whose expectations may be perfectionistic.)

These sensitivities may lend strength to defensive reactions against incestuous invitations to obliterate boundaries between psychiatrists and pastors at the philosophical level. Lest pastors feel alienated by controversy, however, they should be aware that the boundaries between schools of psychoanalytic orientation are as peaceful and defensive as was the Maginot line. Controversy between "neo-Freudians" and "true Freudians" by contrast turns the stubborn isolationism of the old folk song, "I'm a Methodist, Methodist in my belief, I'm a Methodist til I die" into a ditty suitably to be sung at World Church Councils.

Murder has already been hinted at in sublimative form. In spite of his apologists, when Freud saw religion as a universal neurosis, or religious belief as an outgrowth of a personal neurosis, he was calling a spade a spade as *he* examined the cards. To some religious believers, unless they cannibalistically digest away the undesirable, Freud's relegation of religion to unresolved infantile problems, knocks the chip off their shoulders. Freud's conclusions were, whether accurate or not, whether well intended or not, inflammatory. As a patient put it recently, "Call me anything you like—stupid, selfish, stubborn, sinful—but don't call me sick!" Left-overs from Freud's attacks for the milieu of psychiatry and religion are mutual distrust and convictions that the opposite camp's intents are destructive. The fears, apprehensions, and hostility make the setting like the simmering vigilance of opponents in a Holy War.

But why such gross reactions which appear to be sublimations of the primitive crimes—cannibalism, incest, and murder? Why such heat? It is to this point that our study has some pertinence. It indicated that prejudices, beliefs, and one's philosophy of life are precipitates of an individual's total life experience, not just his philosophical or religious exposure. His early formative years which shaped his character and gives his personality uniqueness, as well as his current psychological status are determinative of his personal *weltanschauung*. If there are literally millions of choices that finally add up to a life philosophy one calls his own, these choices are made in a fashion influenced and determined by his individuality of experience and character. Thus, although there are clusters of beliefs expressed in formal denominations or philosophies, the tenets of these structured systems are interpreted *individually* and uniquely. Philosophies of life in their careful assessment, are not Roman Catholic, Jewish, Baptist, Buddhist, Rogerian, Aristotilian, Bergsonian, or Freudian. They are John Jonesian, Bill Smithian and Joe Doaksian. Thus, an ingestion of (cannibalism), a seduction to abandon (incest), or an attack on (murder), one's "principles" are not simply received as neutral stimuli that challenge a satisfying life philosophy. These assaults strike the *person* himself and he responds with the antagonism appropriate to a personal attack. He is then no longer defending Freud or defending God—he is defending himself!

It is always tempting for discoverers who find keys that fit many locks to assume, after they have repeatedly tested the key in many familiar doors, that the key fits all doors. But keys to mysteries of unconscious behavior in individuals (as in our study) do not necessarily fit systems of thought or philosophical mysteries. If the scientist enters the philosophical arena, he must *know* it and come prepared to use the discipline and tools of philosophy—not clinical evidence and inferences. Equally important, the theologian must not drape a philosophical mantle around clinical data. He must keep alert lest his philosophy unwittingly enters to offer a source of distortion in his conclusions.

An example of the potent influence of bias can be dissected from a brilliant biography of Freud by Ernest Jones. His three-volume work is a rich resource, and the author shows no fear in revealing Freud as he saw him—foibles and all. But Jones not only admired Freud; he loved him. As richly as his biography contributes to our knowledge of Freud, it is Jonesian and is influenced by his positive attachment. Freud repeatedly suffered with writer's cramp, a psychosomatic symptom. Freud himself attributed it to psychological disturbance and in writing to Marie Bonaparte states, "Perhaps it will interest you to learn (and to see) that my handwriting has come back to what it used to be. For weeks it was disturbed as the result of my last attack of urinary trouble which is now subsiding. There is an inner (psychological) connection between urinating and writing and assuredly not only with me. When I first noticed the signs of prostatic hypertrophy in the functioning of the bladder, in 1909 in New York, I suffered at the same time from writer's cramp, a condition foreign to me until then."[7] Jones, momentarily leaving his objectivity aside, in Volume II, p. 392, indicated that Freud had "rheumatism." "This would be apt to attack his right hand and make writing difficult. It is also not surprising with someone so addicted to the use of the pen that there were occasional attacks of writer's cramp."(!) For Jones, his hero's symptom occurred because he wrote so much, an explanation not acceptable to Freud himself. I cite this example to demonstrate the ease by which we can apply the rules of our own discipline when we see fit and when it furthers or defends our own personal point of view.

Conflicting systems of theory and philosophy that bring the sublimated effects of cannibalism, incest, and murder are in our midst. They are part of the milieu of psychiatry and pastoral care. But fortunately, these destructive urges appear to be more than counterbalanced by a spirit of goodwill and mutual curiosity that guides those who take the trouble to become personally involved with members of "that other profession."

It is a curious thing that in spite of Freud's attacks on religion, one of his regular and most cherished correspondents was Pastor Oskar Pfister.[8] From their exchanges it is plain they had mutual respect, admiration, and the kind of relationship that left room for controversy and independent philosophy. Both seemed devoted to the search

[7] Ernest Jones, M.D., *The Life and Work of Sigmund Freud*, Vol. III (New York: Basic Books, Inc., Publishers, 1957), p. 236.

[8] *Psychoanalysis and Faith, the Letters of Sigmund Freud and Oskar Pfister*, edited by Heinrich Meng and Ernst Freud, translated by Eric Mosbacher (London: Hogarth Press and the Institute of Psycho-analysis, 1963).

for truth whether it took one (Pfister) to the side of men who fell off mountains to learn their dying thoughts or the other to the side of men who lay on the couch to learn the workings of the mind. Perhaps their collaborative spirit in the search for truth and the service of man could serve as a lasting model for all of us interested in psychiatry and pastoral care.

The intent of this work is not to becloud further the milieu wherein psychiatry and pastoral care are already sufficiently burdened with the fiery feelings of sublimated cannibalism, incest, and murder. It is not intended to convert anyone, alienate further these two fields of endeavor, or offer short-cuts to a pseudo-psychiatry for pastors. My attempt, rather, is aimed at bringing pastors, in particular, to a greater appreciation of their natural resources so that these can be of service whether they rest in the strengths and uses of their own personalities or the great resources of their religion.

CHAPTER TWO

PASTORAL DIAGNOSIS

Diagnosis has been a formulation as familiarly associated with medicine as the Hippocratic oath. Long before the advent of scientific medicine, the arts and the skills of the physician have been associated with his capacity to make a diagnosis on which to base proper treatment. In any age of the history of medicine, the "quack" has been the healer who prescribes without a diagnosis. With the coming of modern medicine, diagnosis plays a major part in training. The medical student begins his study by placing diagnostic principles in the warp and woof of his medical thinking. Before the student becomes a therapist he must first become a diagnostician. For many competent medical schools an unspoken but firm doctrine concerning the student's education reads: "Soon enough the student will learn the ways and means of treatment—let him first become competent in diagnosis."

The Rationale of Pastoral Diagnosis

The years of study in the basic sciences as well as those in his clerkship are constructed to give the student-physician an understanding of his patient and diseases. He learns to take a careful, useful history, to use his senses and his mind to effect a discerning physical examination and to call upon the laboratory appropriately to give him answers to the most important question presented to him by each patient—the diagnosis. It is not perfidious to the tradition of medicine for the physician to invest his energies in developing his skills in diagnosis for one basic reason: *proper treatment depends on correct diagnosis.*

Before we look at the possible usefulness of the concept of "pastoral diagnosis" it would be worthwhile to take a step further in examining the importance and meaning of diagnosis in medicine. An appropriate place to start is with the *American Illustrated Medical Dictionary* by W. A. N. Dorland.[1] Dorland explains that diagnosis has its roots in two Greek words: "dia" meaning between or apart, plus "gnosis" or knowledge; or from the root word in literal translation, knowledge to distinguish between. The first formal definition he gives is, "the art of distinguishing one disease from another." His second reads, "the determination of the nature of a case of disease." He states that a tentative diagnosis is "a diagnosis based upon the available sources of information, but subject to change."

To illustrate the importance of the proposition, "proper treatment depends on correct diagnosis," an example may be of value. An accurate diagnosis may mean literally the difference between life and death for a patient. A man who comes wheezing into a physician's office too short of breath to talk must receive the benefit of the physician's correct diagnosis if he is to meet relief and not the Reaper; if he is to live and not die. For the foolish physician to assume the man's asthma is cardiac and not bronchial might result in "treatment" with an injection of morphine. For the bronchial asthmatic this could precipitate a prompt demise. The *same* drug administered to the cardiac asthmatic is likely to offer relief and the beginning interruption of his cardiac failure. Thus, morphine, given for two types of difficult breathing, brings opposite results.

The astute physician will of course not only have immediately differentiated these two types of asthma, he will also not be content until he understands the exact nature of the patient's difficulty *and* its etiology or cause. If he arrives at a working diagnosis of congestive heart failure, he will use means to relieve the patient, but his work is not done. He must learn the cause of the heart failure. Is it secondary to rheumatic heart disease? Arteriosclerotic heart disease? Myxedema (thyroid deficiency)? Beriberi (vitamin deficiency)? Cerebral insult (vascular brain injury)? He must decide amongst these and other possibilities if he is to be of more than transient help

[1] 21st Edition (Philadelphia: W. B. Saunders Company, 1949), p. 424.

to the patient in cardiac failure even though his operational diagnosis is certain.

In order to be confident of proper treatment, he continues to employ his diagnostic skills after his initial work in a careful follow-up that includes a persistent observation of the *effects* of instituted treatment. His diagnostic acumen is not lulled to sleep. Has the prescribed and appropriate treatment given the results expected? "If not, why not?" becomes once again a diagnostic question. The discerning physician may under certain conditions aim to treat symptoms—but he also knows why he does so. Treating symptoms when there may be a specific cure available is a medical tragedy.

No one is likely to dispute the importance of diagnosis for the physician—but for the pastor? Is *he* to be a diagnostician?[2] *Webster's Collegiate Dictionary* presents the possibilities for a broader and perhaps applicable concept of diagnosis with the definition, "the decision reached."[3] It is my conviction that the pastor no less than the doctor has the responsibility of performing diagnostic duties and reaching a decision before he begins therapeutic action.

Before pursuing the concept of pastoral diagnosis it may be helpful to pause a moment to examine an aspect of the "image" of the modern clergyman. The day of automatic respect for members of most of the professions, especially members of the ministry, is disappearing if not slipped by altogether. In our individual work with pastors we have seen some struggling to find their identity and fulfillment as professionals, to learn how to implement a "vital," "dynamic" church program that will exert a leadership and not a followship. But most pertinent to our discussion we find in some overworking pastors a powerful urge that superficially, at least, always looks good: the desire to help people.

Let us not be misunderstood to complain about the clergy's historical capacity for compassion, but rather to point out that the desire to help does not always lead to efficacious results. The warmest, sincerest most dedicated intern in a busy receiving ward cannot allow

---

[2] See Rev. Rollin J. Fairbanks' article "Diagnosis in Pastoral Care" in *The Journal of Pastoral Care;* Vol. 6, Spring, 1952, p. 34.

[3] Fifth Edition (Springfield, Mass.: G. & C. Merriam Co., 1946), p. 277.

his wishes to alleviate pain or discomfort to interfere with a careful formulated diagnostic conclusion. The minister, in his desire to establish his church and himself as positive forces in the world cannot rely on his wish to help people alone as the means for effecting salvation of others and himself. The wish to help may, paradoxically, border on the dangerous when it springs from a self-protective device whose latent meaning is "let me help you so I'll know my role, my profession, my calling and preserve my integrity."

In any of the professions, including psychiatry, there should be no contentment with the wish to help, unless this desire of the heart becomes linked with the judicious use of the head. To make clear by illustration how compassion unexamined or untutored may lead to harm and not help, I would like to cite the following excerpt from the therapy done by a psychiatric resident I have had the privilege of supervising. (I use the word privilege not politely, but to indicate my opinion of him as sensitive, growing in skills, dedicated, and possessing the wish to help.) The patient was characterologically an obsessive compulsive character; one of his problems was an overwhelmingly tight control over and defense against an awareness of the expression of his aggressive feelings. He was troubled by the common fear of those who bridle tightly their emotions: to have aggressive wishes creates the dangerous possibility of destruction of others. Inroads against this leftover of childhood omnipotence were being made. In one particular interview however, the patient came reluctantly through bad weather, complaining of a bothersome cold. He had an upper respiratory infection that was obvious, giving him a feverish appearance and the therapy hour was punctuated by coughing, sniffling, and sneezing. But the hour was loaded, too, with latent criticism of the therapist. As the interview headed in time toward a conclusion, the patient's criticisms were approaching a hitherto unexpressed degree of openness. About 10 minutes before the end of the scheduled hour, the patient sneezed and had a nose-blow, no different than the coryzal symptoms earlier in the hour. Suddenly the resident psychiatrist was struck with "compassion." He asked the patient if he were feeling so uncomfortable that he would like to leave early, and, to their mutual relief, the patient thought it an excellent idea and gratefully adjourned. After the next therapeutic hour the resident honestly confessed he felt in a sea of confusion and sought supervisory consultation. Indeed the following hour did seem confused. Themes in the patient's communications and his emotional stance reflected sullenness, disappointment, guilt, and isolation. To try and understand the confused hour we looked at the hour before. It began to be clear to both of us about the same time what had happened. The resident began to suspect his "reasons" for dismissing the patient early: the bad weather would not be changed, no matter when the patient left; leaving 10 minutes early would mean no less time away from home, nor improve his cold; he had made it to the hour, did he need "help" making it home? With a flash of recognition, and a spot of courage the resident said, "I thought I was being kind, and all the time I was defending myself against his anger."

To be sure, this was not an irreparable error, and the psycho-therapeutic process continued to a successful termination. But if error there was, it was in the area of assessment of the situation, with an incorrect "decision reached." Although we would not quarrel with those who would contend that this judgment came in the framework of treatment, a kind of diagnostic thinking precedes action whether the action be a psychotherapeutic interpretation, an act of compassion, a referral, reading scripture at the bedside, or offering a prayer with one in crisis. In the case cited, the psychiatric resident's ingrained "helping reflex," together with a defensive move away from the patient's criticism, overpowered a more useful therapeutic measure: to stay with the patient in facing the latter's neurotic fear of his own hostile wishes.

Although it has been implicit in our discussion, let us be explicit: the minister's desire to help, a *sine qua non* for pastoral care, may paradoxically stand in his way. This may come about by an unexamined impulse to help prompted by some defensiveness aroused as noted with our respectable psychotherapist above. With the rise of pastoral care into the foreground of the minister's work, there has grown a "helping reflex" quick as a lawman's draw, taking a bead on every pastoral challenge no matter what the situation and firing the panacea, "pastoral counseling!" This currently popular pastoral tool has its place—and a place of great importance—in the work of a minister, but it may be no more indicated in a particular pastoral situation than a teeth-rattling sermon, an invective against segregation, or the singing of carols with the youth fellowship.

The modern minister is not eager to be trapped in a professional dead-end, like patent medicine men who offered perhaps tasty but ineffective concoctions for every ill. He is aware of his high calling, the urgency of his message, the profundity of his armamentarium— and at the same time must guard against dissatisfaction with his achievements. Although the concept of pastoral diagnosis seems peculiarly suited to the ministry of pastoral care, we are struck with its possibilities in the whole functioning of the ministry. No truly useful sermon for instance is preached without a proper evaluation of the needs of the congregation. No pastoral prayer, no scriptural reading, no hospital call can bring the rewards of spiritual enlargement without an analysis of the needs at hand.

Someone has likened the seminary experience of the young theologian to that of a man who enters a long, deep cave, carefully guarding a lighted candle, and in the depths of the cave finds someone has blown it out. The analogy could mean many things. To use it for our purposes, if the student comes to training for the ministry out of some heartwarming religious experience, he is likely to feel out of his experience that he has found *the* brand of pastoral "treatment" to offer sick souls. As he encounters the winds and storms of philosophical and theological controversy his world may be enlarged but the adequacy of his "treatment" for human ills, that looked so fulfilling for others, as it had been for himself, fades. The individual gospels of his professors and his fellow students impinge until, like the fabled but deceived dog over the water, he drops his bone to reach for an image. It strikes us that in contrast to medical training, theological education is geared to treatment of human need, not diagnosis; to proclamation without assessment; to action without analysis of its object's needs.

Although we have indicated previously that pastoral diagnosis may be a concept useful beyond the field of pastoral care, its specific formulation unfolds most clearly in this field.

What then is pastoral diagnosis? Its flavor is reflected in Jesus' injunction to the disciples, "Be ye therefore wise as serpents and harmless as doves." (Matthew 10:16) Traditionally, wisdom has been associated with the aged; but it appears more likely to be the accrual of a special kind of knowledge developed in a man who has dipped fully into life experiences, and who, with each encounter, profitably learns about his world, his fellow man, and himself. There are old people who are foolish, and young who seem wise. Wisdom is not an inherited genetic trait. It depends at least, in part, on assimilated training. Acknowledging that there seem to be gifted, intuitive souls, we are convinced that disciplined powers of observation, understanding, and integration of experience contribute to what may appear to be intuitive capacities for pastoral diagnosis.

Pastoral diagnosis is an orderly, structured approach to pastoral problems which taps all the resources of the minister, including his compassion (heart) and his objectivity (head). It eventuates in a tentative conclusion as to what the trouble is, opening the way for appropriate action (pastoral treatment). Ideally, the pastor will not be overinfluenced by the symptoms (subjective complaints) of his parishioner to the exclusion of the signs (objective signals of disturbance). The proposition that proper treatment rests on correct diagnosis should serve the pastor as usefully as the physician.

Unfortunately in our culture there are no diagnostic centers for human needs. There are centers that announce by their title which human needs they are interested in serving, such as Lighthouse for the Blind, Child and Family Service, Vocational Training, Mental Health Clinics, Travelers' Aid, and others. But in the professions, the minister has no equal for the variety of human needs he is asked to meet. He rarely has a referral sent him that gives an inkling of what is ahead. He is forced to become, himself, a diagnostician of human needs.

Psychological Vectors of Pastoral Diagnosis

Requests for help which tap a pastor's diagnostic acumen range from the social, moral, cultural, educational, artistic, economic, and specifically religious petitions over to the psychological ones. Naturally, our focus will be on the psychological factors which may play a role in pastoral diagnosis. To sharpen this focus means to lay aside for the *duration* of this monograph those other equally important aspects that, of course, enter broad pastoral diagnostic considerations. To silhouette the psychological factors, we would like to employ the admittedly limited values of analogy, making over, momentarily, a man into a plant.

For the farmer to be a successful agriculturalist, he must have an appreciation of the importance of the soil (culture) and climate (family) on the potentialities of the seed (genes). He will need to know what to expect from a normally developing plant (maturation and personality development). Besides these rather crucial aspects in the life of the plant, the farmer is expected to know something about the plant itself (personality, character) after maturation. What are its strengths and weaknesses, its susceptibilities, its assets, its flower and fruit? Finally, if the farmer is to be of assistance, he must know something of the possible pathology to which the plant may be subject (signs and symptoms of disturbance). He will know what kind of bugs will attack it or what signs of blight can be read. Although many of these aspects of understanding may appear to come naturally to a successful farmer, few in our days of modern farming would dispute the importance of education and training for the man of the soil, even for the farmer who has "the feel" for agriculture.

It is beyond the scope of this work to deal fully with any one aspect of the psychology of the individual, but some enlargement is called for.

The soil. Ministers are generally equipped to understand our culture. The issues of importance in our time are at least as familiar to the minister as they are to other professionals. The prophetic note of the "still, small voice" is small, still, but it is not absent. By the nature of his office and his calling, the minister aligns himself with forces that fight cultural sickness. But, in the framework of pastoral care for the individual, prophetic roars out-decibel bleating of sheep gone astray. It is our impression, that assessment of social ills is not blighted by unexploitive attention to individuals. Although a side effect of perceptive listening may be the sharpening of one's prophetic tools, our object is to focus on the individual's cultural milieu with only one intent, namely to understand *him*.

One of the most difficult but fascinating problems of diagnosis for the psychiatrist presents itself in this very area. In my own experience it has only been after prolonged observation that one is able to determine with certain patients whether the pathology observed stems from an intrapsychic difficulty or from the stamp of the individual's culture or both. A Black Muslim, in a fit of rage, suddenly began to destroy his immediate surroundings and to attack whites or blacks who attempted to restrain him. Finally he was brought, subdued by four large orderlies, to a security room of the acutely disturbed ward of a psychiatric hospital. His frenzy persisted until his pastor, "Mr. X," arrived. The patient became immediately docile, and sullenly cooperative. The impact of his leader's presence, soothing words, and mild admonitions transformed a maniacal, homicidal patient into one who was quiet, though still distant and cold. The problem, of course, was to determine first of all how sick this man was. Was he reflecting a cultural, but understandable extreme? Was his behavior consistent with this culture's behavior or feelings? Was this extremist group a convenient hat rack on which to hang his intrapsychic, psychotic disturbance? Or was it all of these things? Diagnostic problems, wherein it is equally difficult to separate personal from cultural pathology, include "cabin fever psychosis"; "hillbilly psychosis"; "Texas psychosis"; and "Madison Avenue psychosis."

Culture can be thought of as a precipitate of accumulated human experience which engulfs and guides individuals within it. It offers its own behavioral norms and, therefore, its own definitions of mental sickness. Psychiatric attention has been focused on the individual, but more recently on the family with social psychiatry ever widening our gaze. In our own culture, most psychiatrists still do not attribute mental disease to cultural disturbance, but vice versa. It is thought that the emotionally disturbed gravitate to form their own cultures voluntarily whether in the blighted sections of cities without organization, or in extremist groups which live out their problems in "acceptable" organizations. Our knowledge is far too juvenile even to consider a percentage estimate of the role of culture in mental disorder.

The climate. The second and exceedingly crucial psychological aspect in pastoral diagnosis of the individual is his family background. If we are to stay close to our current theme of pastoral diagnosis of the individual, we must now deal with his family in quite a constricted sense—namely, the impact of the emotional climate (parents and siblings) on the development of the individual in our attention. (For the moment we must put aside a broader discussion of the importance of the family as it is considered a unit for study in and of itself. Concepts of "family diagnosis" involve more than a single individual and are, therefore, not in the focus of our immediate task.)

Horace Bushnell, a century ago in *Nature and Nurture,* reported his impressions of the family as a determinant of the spiritual life of the individual. Students of human nature, whether their stripe be anthropologist, sociologist, or psychologist have been forced to acknowledge the powerful influence of the family on its child members. The potency of the emotional climate of the psycho-biological-social unit similarly forces us to devote attention to it as a contributor to diagnostic understanding. Our momentary goal is to attempt to underline the formative power of the family by citing recent research, secondly by assaying the minister's diagnostic role in this particular vector of individual evaluation and finally by presenting a case illustration.

There is far too little space to give adequate representation of the vast fingers of investigation of the vital forces affecting the child that stem from his family milieu. This means we are forced to present illustrative rather than comprehensive studies.

For sheer impact, Spitz's study on "hospitalism" has few competitors.[4] The study does make a strong case for the strength and power of the mother-child relationship which can be viewed as the earliest and perhaps central climate or milieu at the individual's life start. What, in brief, Spitz did was to study the effects on infants whose climate

[4] Rene A. Spitz, "Hospitalism. An Inquiry into the Genesis of Psychiatric Conditions in Early childhood," *The Psychoanalytic Study of the Child,* Vol. I, International University Press, N.Y., 1945, p. 53.

was to all intents and purposes motherless. Two nursery situations presented themselves to him for comparison. In one the physical care was "sterile" both literally and emotionally. That is, one group of children was provided food, shelter, clean surroundings—but no mothering. Only the barest time was spent with each child for physical purposes of his care, performed by various individuals. In the other group, sanitation, cleanliness, and other externals did not compare as favorably with the first group—but each child had a mother or single mother substitute.

The absence of mothering care, in short, had disastrous effects. The survivors of the sterile group four years later were a pitiful group indeed. Many of them were considered psychotic; and the healthiest, severely neurotic. Skills such as walking and talking were but primitively developed and it appeared likely that none of them would be destined to live a reasonably normal life. Perhaps even more striking was the malignant effect of motherlessness on survival. The mortality rate was far out of proportion in spite of good physical surroundings and available medical care. Spitz's study makes it clear: the absence of mothering to the infant appears to be not only disastrous, but deadly.

A family implies a mother and father. The study cited above was not described with the intention of derogation of the father to secondary importance. As many contributions as have been made to the understanding of the early mother-child relationships, the father's influence which may be a potent one on that stage of life remains largely unassessed. It is not difficult to conceive, for example, a disturbed mother-child relationship at least partly consequent to a disturbed mother-father relationship. In general, the father's role in the family for the most part is considered to reach more direct importance to child development after a year or two, when the child's world moves from a diadic to a triadic one.

Acknowledging our illustrative rather than comprehensive intent, we wish to make mention of the work of Gregory Bateson, et al., with the most malignant of mental illnesses—schizophrenia.[5] The etiology of this disease is unknown, but these workers present a most interesting theory of psychological causation. Studying the relationships between schizophrenic patients and their mothers, they have observed a phenomenon wherein the mother presents two commands to the child at the same time, one an overt message and the other covert, which puts the child in the position of a "double bind." In this double bind situation the mother is commanding at the same time, "come close" and "stay away"; "love me" and "fear me"; "do" and "don't." If we speak in homespun terms, the mother treats her child like a driver who puts his car in gear and steps firmly on accelerator and brake simultaneously. In one respect this would seem to be the ultimate in hypocrisy except that the "schizophrenogenic mother" is unaware of her binding power.

Double bind impositions can be seen in less malignant and somewhat different forms in the church as well as in the family climate. "Do as I say and not as I do" is as familiar a saying to the pastor as those parents who insist on their child's having a religious education —at the Sunday School. There are probably few churches without at least one or two old-time "hypocrites." These few, of course, are the "reason" other types of self-deceivers do not go to church!

Child psychiatrists are familiar with parents who appear to the world as controlled, law-abiding, contributive citizens whose children may be "holy terrors," or put more professionally, delinquent. One of the kinds of delinquency that has been understood stems from double messages conveyed to children. In this situation, the troublesome behavior of the youngster appears to gain stimulus from parents' wishes which they, themselves, neither act on nor perceive as their own. For example, a teen-age boy I saw recently was brought to the clinic by alarmed parents who complained, "We're afraid Bobby's gonna get a girl into a family way." Not only were they putting extraordinary limits on him in a kind of straitjacket supervision, they were constantly badgering him with questions about his sexual life. Daily, both were keeping track of the boy's masturbatory activities by examining the bed sheets—with the boy's knowledge! It is, of course, not incidental that the boy's own father and new stepmother had been married but three months and were expecting their first child in a like number of months!

Double messages, of course, may not emanate from a single parent as described above but there may be two messages equally opposite, one from each parent. A youngster so beleaguered in this situation must struggle not only with an impossible choice but with a host of his own wishes and inhibitions that rise out of early life development struggles. The latter are problem enough for any child, but when a choice of action may mean loving one parent at the cost of losing or alienating the other, a third alternative of an anti-social or self-defeating nature seems safer to him.

Devastating too, may be alternating messages characterized by changing intensity of expectations from one or both parents. Multiple reasons for such inconsistencies include: periodic father-mother differences which are played out on the family gridiron with the child as football; intermittent seizures of guilt in the parent; and changes in the psychic economy of the parents. To exemplify the latter, when energies are dissipated into a depressive episode, a mother's ordinarily constructive prohibitive stance may degenerate into, "What's the use? I don't care. Let him do what he wants." In these "alternating message" families the emotional climate is completely unpredictable.

But what of pastoral pertinence have we here? The pastor will not be assessing or making diagnostic evaluations of families in the same framework as the specialized investigations and illustrations noted above. In a real way, however, the pastor has long been acquainted with the importance of the family climate. And for those ministers who are not itinerant, there is a decided value in their longitudinal views of families that may add perspective to cross-sectional or immediate evaluations of the family.

Besides the chronological or longitudinal picture of his parish family, the minister is unique in the helping professions in that he is expected to make calls on the homes of his people. Such calls may come easy to some pastors, difficult to others. Some visits may present opportunities for service, while others may evoke a "that-was-a-waste-of-time" feeling. One positive result is available, consequent to almost every visit no matter whether a particular mission is "successful" or "unsuccessful." The pastor gains an impression of the emotional climate of the household. Although he need not write down or even pay special heed to whether the emotional climate in a home is moderate, warm, cold, inconsistent, tempestuous or controlled, an impression is registered. It can serve as one of the vectors that help him to form a tentative diagnosis for any one member of the family whose home he has visited.

CASE ILLUSTRATION. A 19-year-old college student presented himself to the outpatient department of the University of Chicago, Department of Psychiatry with complaints of insomnia, irritability, and inability to concentrate with a recent grade report far below his previous average. The onset of his depression coincided with the discovery that his father had an inoperable cancer. At the completion of his diagnostic interview, as a part of a pilot study he was asked, "What are your ideas about God?" He was doubly shocked. First he was taken aback because a psychiatrist was interested in his religion (!), but secondly he felt confounded that "You, a highly educated and supposedly sophisticated psychiatrist would ask anyone about mythology!" He proceeded to lecture the psychiatrist on "the facts" of religion, asserting he was a thorough going atheist. "Any psychiatrist certainly ought to be acquainted with Freud's assertion that God is a projection of a human father and most certainly there is no evidence that even if a God existed that he would have attributes of goodness, love, or power!" Of interest concerning the climate of his family was that he was an only child whose father had been an irresponsible, rarely present salesman who could never be counted on. When the father was at home he was usually drunk and at those times became combative with the patient's mother. When not drinking, he was extraodinarily submissive not only to the patient's mother but to the patient's own wishes.

Because this is but a case excerpt and not a complete presentation, no dogmatic conclusions can be drawn from so little data. With benefit of all the clinical information, however, the psychiatrist decided the patient was suffering with a depression, precipitated by the assault of illness on the father. Throughout the boy's life there were frequent and strong wishes to do away with the father who commanded so little love and respect. When nature's ax fell on the father, it was as though the patient held the handle. The patient was aware of his guilt only indirectly, since one of his major concerns was that he was "letting Dad down by getting such poor grades." The psychiatrist recognized that it was not sufficient to account for the guilt-ridden depression just because a father developed cancer. He turned to the family climate to augment his understanding. Here the story of the intensely ambivalent relationship with the father especially helped fill in the missing links of diagnostic understanding. From current studies of our own, we are becoming increasingly convinced that family climate is not only crucial in character or personality structure, it also plays an important role in the formation of personal philosophy. For example, with this young man we would be far more likely to consider his belligerent atheism not as a reaction to a poor presentation of religious issues by his church, but as much more intimately associated with his whole life experience, including the turbulent emotional climate of his early years.

The seed. It may appear to be irrelevant to discuss biological genetics in a discourse on pastoral diagnosis. However, it at least deserves mention. People in the helping professions display little if any interest in genes, perhaps because biological inheritance looks like a closed door or water over the dam. "What can we *do* about that!" Although it may be illusional, altering the soil or changing the climate or tending the plant offer "accessible" avenues to help. From a research standpoint, however, the door is not a closed one. Although Kallman's studies on the genetic factors in the etiology of schizophrenia have been subject to serious question,[6] investigations in this field continue to be important research. New technological and methodological approaches have opened paths for, heretofore, inaccessible investigation.

Biological investigations are central in the frontiers of research into mental illness, especially psychoses. But in clinical observations there is no room for haughtiness either on the part of the psychodynamic schools. For example, some clinical investigators are convinced from their studies that the mother-child relationship, so basic to personality development, is not a one-way street that runs only from mother to child. They are convinced that there are not only rejecting

[6] See Donald Jackson's *Etiology of Schizophrenia* (New York: Basic Books, Inc., Publishers, 1960).

mothers, but children who reject as well. They find mothers report-
ing in the history of their disturbed child that from the start of life,
"He wouldn't cuddle," or "He didn't seem to want me. He was
different from my other babies." Whether actually from the start
there was something inherent in the baby that would not permit
mothering by *any* mother is a question that is not easily subject to
investigation. Antagonists of postulated biological or inheritance
factors would assume that for one reason or another this particular
child evoked something in the mother that very early prevented her
from giving her love, eventuating in a mutually rejecting circle.

Another phenomenon of interest that we have observed in our
work with children, could be called the "tree of life" concept. Like
oaks growing out of sidewalk cracks, not only surviving, but changing
the sidewalks, some youngsters who come from unbelievably deprived
situations reflect surprisingly unaccounted-for strengths of adaptation.
None of these youngsters of course are unscarred, but for many their
adaptive power seems altogether out of proportion when one con-
siders the soil and climate that looked inimicable to life itself. The
genetically-oriented observer might assert, "Just good protoplasm";
while the dynamically-oriented observer might speculate, "There must
have been a warm grandmother or wet-nurse back there in his early
years. Or maybe, in his infancy, things were less chaotic in the family
than now. Or, perhaps, an openly rejecting mother who's consistent
in her rejection is a better mother than an ambivalent, covertly rejecting mother."

At any rate, behavioral scientists are a long way from writing the
final chapters on the causative factors in personality development.
Without closing any research doors, it is fair to state that most clinical
psychotherapists base their assessment and treatment on the assumption that the early formative years *are* the determinative ones in
personality development.

Although it is true that there are many psychiatric problems, e.g.
mental deficiency, which are only now beginning to catch researcher's
and therapist's eyes, the really major breakthrough taking place is an
attitudinal one. Public interest in a medical problem, such as polio,
is often the necessary prelude to its solution. We can hope this will

be the case with mental diseases. But a word of caution to pastors and educators against over-optimism is indicated on two counts. First, the precious growing concern of the public cannot be allowed to be dissipated by a backlash of disappointment when major breakthroughs are not soon forthcoming. The challenge is enormous. The reader may recall Dr. Jonas Salk's reply to a question fired at him when his vaccine became famous. "What is the greatest medical problem facing us?" He replied without hesitating, "Mental illness." Great strides are being made but there are miles to be covered which will require sustained public support. Secondly, no matter how favorable developments are in society's attitudes toward mental illness, certain problems offer limited futures for rehabilitation and no prognosis for cure in our current state of knowledge. Unlike most other body organs, brain tissue does not replace itself. Therefore, whether its cause is congenital, secondary to injury, or biochemical change, brain damage is permanent. Also, certain mental conditions, in which no brain damage has been demonstrated, appear to be well nigh irreversible. For some individuals, "all the King's horses" are still not enough. The pastor may have to help interpret such conditions or be willing to face this tragedy with his parishioner or relatives. In the meantime, until new discovery unlocks etiological mysteries, humane, optimistic care directed toward the fullest possible adaptation for those with injured brains or twisted minds must prevail.

The developing plant. It is far beyond the intent of this monograph to present details of child development. The following skimpy treatment of the subject in no way, however, reflects my degree of respect for its importance. The intent here will be toward fitting this vector into the scheme of pastoral diagnosis. Any clergyman interested in the pastoral care of his people will find a useful framework, tailored to his own needs, for understanding how a normal person grows up emotionally, how growth can be stunted, and how such stunting lives on in people who chronologically and physically are matured.[7]

No time offers greater vulnerability to the plant than the occasion

[7] Two classic descriptions of development are: Freud, *op. cit.*, "Three Essays on the Theory of Sexuality," Vol. VII, pp. 135 ff. and Erik Erikson, *Childhood and Society* (New York: W. W. Norton & Co., Inc., 1950).

when its first tender sprouts push through the earth. If a plant *ever* needs attention, it is early. Without protection and all that accompanies tender care it will often, like the children in the "sterile" group of Spitz's nursery study, die. Although it appears obvious that a baby that is literally abandoned without rescue will die, it is not so plain that the same child can be emotionally abandoned and can emotionally die or be crippled without the possibility of repair. This is a "hard saying," not easily accepted by those who sometimes imply in the face of tragedy, "All things are possible with the Lord," or "A man can be born again." With our current knowledge there *are* unfortunately people with mental illness who will never be well; helped perhaps, but never well. But this is a diagnostic responsibility the pastor never has to assume any more than he would decide that a newborn is mongoloid.

Normal steps in emotional growth, described by Freud as "psychosexual development," are associated with normal chronological stages of childhood. These steps are as familiar to the well-trained psychiatrist as bodily maturation is to the pediatrician. One of the psychiatrist's responsibilities is to be able to make a cross-sectional evaluation of his patient. Visualization of personality stunting can be discerned as clearly by him as the botanist may read the effects of a bad year in studying the growth rings of a tree. It is not the matter of the moment to discuss whether growth inhibitions can be changed or not, but rather to note that they continue to exert a living real effect in the life of the matured individual.

As with the other diagnostic vectors already mentioned and those to come, the pastor is not expected to be expert in personality development. Rather, he will enlarge his capabilities not simply by an expansion of his knowledge but by putting to better functional use those observations of "human nature" he has made, but not integrated into his diagnostic thinking.

Modern concepts of child development pay heavy debt to Freud's clinical and theoretical concepts of "infantile sexuality." Besides the familiar steps of development he called the "oral," "anal," "phallic," "latency," and "genital" stages, his theory and observations have permitted us to gain a dynamic rather than static perspective. His breakthrough allows us to grasp the continuing live impact of early traumas on the adult.

Of most use for our purposes is his formulation of the "fixation-regression" axes. Freud liked to use analogies which have limited but distinct descriptive value. Freud considered stages of psycho-sexual development to be similar to an advancing army that for one reason or another must leave a certain number of men at each position gained. He assumed that with emotional life there is an energetic ("economic") system represented in the analogy. If, for example, during the first stage of development, the oral stage,* a certain number of troops (psychological energies) have to remain behind at the first position, this permits fewer troops of the now reduced army to deal with the problems of the anal stage.* * Such troop-energy investments along the pathway of growing up could make accessible for use then only a certain number of troops or energies available to meet life's stresses in the later years. If there were a stormy, deprived, or overindulged oral stage, Freud would have considered such an individual to be "fixed" at the oral stage, with most of the person's adult energies still consumed in infantile issues. If, however, advances beyond so primitive an emotional development were made, the child moves normally through the oral and anal stages, and makes a sweep into the Oedipal or phallic stage.* * * "Enemy assaults" (stress or traumas) there can produce a hasty retreat to the safety, comfort, and security bastions of the oral stage. This retreat to a less mature position Freud called "regression." According to his analogy, the healthy, emotionally well-developed adult would, of course, have more troops (energy) to apply usefully to the stresses encountered in life. Thus, the fewer energies bound up with problems appropriately solved early in life, the greater the likelihood of success at the front. His assumption was that no individual's emotional development is complete. The most emotionally developed person under ordinary life stress requires retreats of temporary nature, like sleep, rest, vacations. It becomes possible with this troop analogy to understand more easily why

* Period of infancy, birth to approximately one year.
** Training period, age one to three.
*** Period of the "family romance," age four to six.

certain traumas for one individual may bring about altogether different effects for another. The schizophrenic patient, for example, who is considered "fixed" at the oral stage, though he may appear to be making a satisfactory life adjustment, may, nevertheless, fall apart at his "ego seams" with an incident that to others may appear innocuous or even invisible. It is the psychiatrist's job to know, with expertness, his patient's psycho-sexual development including assessment of his fixation-regression axes.

But what about the pastor? Besides having some kind of useful theoretical framework of personality development, he must also use and depend on his specific knowledge of his parishioners to be able to make useful judgments to guide his own actions and the activity of the Church in relationship to his people. For example, he may have come to recognize that one or two of his shut-ins are sufficiently dependent on him for spiritual food that his vacations require substitutive help to them. He may have noticed that minor or even ordinarily imperceptible changes in the service of worship rouses an inner storm in certain individuals that seems altogether disproportionate. He can seldom fail to notice that certain of his parishioners must think of themselves as first in his eyes while others shrink from his attention. He has noted "children" old enough to have their own who cannot separate themselves from their mothers.

We have encountered ministers who consume their energies in programs of pastoral care instituted without benefit of this particular vector of pastoral diagnosis. No human being always spends his energies wisely or efficiently, but the pastor who continually lays aside his judgment to heed persistently his impulsive desires to help may soon find himself cynical. There are few more "cynicogenic" experiences than repeated emotional investment in causes that bear no fruit or offer no tangible results other than an aching back.

The permanently mentally retarded infant is no less a child of God than his intellectually endowed twin. The good mother is likely to love one no less than the other, but because she is a good mother she will expect different things from them, will recognize what kind of energies are to be expressed to bring each to his fullest potential and gratification. Since her total mothering capacities are finite, she would be doing herself and both children a great injustice to spend her energies in trying to teach the retarded child calculus, or trying to equalize their mentalities by discouraging or depreciating the normal child's mental efforts. Both need her love, care, and attention—geared to their needs and capacities.

Fortunately, most pastors are "goodhearted." Though his good-heartedness may frequently carry the field in meeting the needs of his parishioners, bereft of diagnostic acumen, it may work a disservice to the pastor and his church. It may not be easy for the pastor to recognize as troubled the person who charms, appears to be considerate, and has "lots of personality." But, he has become increasingly sophisticated in spotting people who blatantly use his goodheartedness against themselves and him. It may take a few episodes of being "stung" or disappointed before the pastor recognizes that these characteristics may serve destructive ends, not only for the person in his attention but for the pastor himself. The successful "con man" knows that his personality art, used to manipulate others, finally evokes rage in and rejection by his victim. For a few pastors who are super-idealistic, it takes repeated episodes before they become no longer an easy mark; for others closer to earth, the feeling of being used may be an early signal that alerts them to wider diagnostic assessment, before they leap in to "help."

But the "psychopath," whose personality development is considered little more advanced than the schizophrenic, is a relatively rare problem for the pastor. A far more common example of a crippled personality is the extraordinarily dependent person whose needs, though appealing, are boundless. Like some orphaned waifs who seize the heart strings, they appear to be hungry for human love but some, alas, have insatiable appetites. The pastor's expectations of his own "goodheartedness" may prompt strong feelings of guilt in him if he does not persistently and continually feed such a one who cries out continually for help. But if his diagnostic acumen asserts itself, the pastor will recognize that it is no kinder to quicken the infantile hopes of such dependent people into thinking that at last all their needs will be met by him than it is to permit himself to be conned. It is hardly to be called rejection when the astute pastor recognizes early he can never, ever supply personally (nor could any other one individual) what is missing in the life of such an individual. Though most of us have strong parental interests, none of us can literally replace or fill the vacuum left in someone else's life by a defective or absent mother and/or father. It is true that the *Church* may offer one of the few satisfying havens of concern to such individuals. But the pastor is not free of the diagnostic responsibility to come first to a conclusion regarding the infinite requests of such a person before he offers himself as "counselor." For counselor, in translation, means to the dependent one, "I-will-meet-all-your-needs." Can he, as pastor to a large congregation, be *the* instrument of help for these adult "little ones"? A pastor who makes himself responsible for the needs of two or three such infantile parishioners may find time for little else. Individuals with such overwhelming internal vacuums rarely discriminate "from whence cometh their help." If the Church itself or its various offices and services do not offer enough, the pastor can sometimes dilute the pressure of demand by enlisting other members of the congregation eager to have their efforts appreciated—transiently.

Touching as we are now on "pastoral treatment," before we address ourselves formally to this concept, it is appropriate to consider one type of pastoral treatment in relationship to personality development. Conversion is a powerful instrument that many ministers consider basic in their armamentarium of pastoral treatment. The effects of conversion are sometimes dramatic, impressive, and long lasting. At times the results of a sound conversion may approach the miraculous. There are instances in which an extraordinary sinner has become an extraordinary saint as, for example, St. Augustine; or a vigorous persecutor, the vigorously persecuted; a haughty Pharisee, the "chief of sinners" (St. Paul); a strong bound character, a strong freed character (Wesley). These men all did an abrupt "about face" from men of sin to men of grace. But insofar as such cases have been or can be studied, there is no evidence that their basic personality structure was altered through conversion any more than their anatomy or physiology was altered. There may indeed be alterations of behavior as radical as turning from a destructive citizen to a contributive one, but the moulding of character makeup (not moral character) is not shattered. St. Augustine, St. Paul, and Wesley were all quite different personalities from each other, not only before their conversions but afterwards as well. Weak personalities whose energies remained fixed at a primitive level of personality development will, after a sound religious conversion, remain weak personalities. For a variable length of time they may look differently, see things differently, behave differently, but the troops have not moved. "To be born again or become a new man in Christ" will not convert, will not change an obsessive-compulsive personality to an hysterical personality, or vice versa. To our knowledge there are no reported cases of schizophrenic patients undergoing a religious conversion who left their schizophrenia behind; or of primitively fixed dependent personalities who next day after conversion had developed psychological maturity.

Perhaps St. Francis of Assisi and his friend St. Juniper best illustrate this point. Both men were soundly converted, but they each continued breathing as they had before. St. Francis, the heir of a good brain and sound raising, after a wild, rebellious adolescence and then conversion, founded the history changing society of the "Little Flowers." St. Juniper, born with questionable intelligence into an emotionally impoverished home, became one of Francis' Little Flowers whose poor judgment was a constant source of embarrassment to his brothers. There was no doubt that his heart was in the right place as his warm benevolence prompted him to give repeatedly his *all* to the poor whether it was the silver chapel bells prized by his colleagues or his clothes to become a (naked) "fool for Christ." The pastor's judgment of the assessment of his parishioners' needs cannot depend on the quality or quantity of parishioners' conversion experiences. If he is to care, in the pastoral sense, he will give some heed to the factors of emotional development to make accurate assessments.

The pastor need not be and should not be an expert in personality development. Neither does it appear profitable that he be oblivious or naive to its importance. Apart from enlarging his knowledge by study, the pastor does have the perspective of knowing the circumstances of development for many of his parishioners. A rule of thumb by which he can gauge grossly this aspect of pastoral diagnosis comes in answer to a question. "How strong is the resistance of the parishioner

to the winds of life's adversities?" Or, put another way, "How successfully does he manage the various qualities and quantities of stress,
and are his adaptations appropriate?" For example, one would not
expect the same degree of turning-in-on-the-self and away from the
world consequent to the loss of a business deal as one might expect
with the loss of the business.

No one is in a better position either than the pastor's for assessment
of the grieving process. He knows it far better than the undertaker,
for grieving is not an episode, but a process. Physicians and chaplains
are often responsible during the immediate loss situation, psychiatrists
become involved with unresolved grief problems, but the day-by-day
work of the pastor gives him unique opportunity to determine
whether any one individual's grief reaction is healthily adequate.
Thus, the manner in which a parishioner faces the death of a loved
one may tell much about his psychological resources, including some
idea of his psychological development. Parental death may be especially illuminative in this regard.

The plant itself.   The artificiality of analogous thinking of a
human being as a plant is complicated by the compartmentalization
into segments of consideration which overlap. We have, in discussing
plant development, taken special note of the importance of development not as a past dead history but as a current live operation in the
adult lives of parishioners. For instance, an adequate grief reaction of
a parishioner for a parent infers the likelihood of a relatively good
relationship, rooted in his early life development. But further, it
may also bespeak the current psychological capacities of the self, or
"ego strength." One such strength is the capacity to express feeling or
emotion appropriately. It can be immediately recognized, however,
that such a characteristic of the plant itself did not spring up over
night. The first teachers of how one handles one's feelings are the
parents.

Recognizing then that we are contending with as much overlap as
in the various stages of psychosexual development, we would, nevertheless, like to enumerate a number of characteristics that reflect the
strength of the self. These include the following:

Quality of human relationships. Consideration of how people get along with each other is hardly foreign territory to the thinking or observations of pastors. "Good will amongst men" has been an aim of most religions and certainly is an emphasis in Judao-Christian traditions. In the pastoral assessment of the strengths of his parishioners, however, the minister looks more closely than simply to make an observation as to whether there be goodwill present or not. He already knows something of the variations possible in the quality of human relationships. He has seen men marry beautiful women who are not loved for themselves but used as display cards; he has noted women marrying moneyed men to satisfy their acquisitive or ambitious desires. He has seen children that are forced to live out the wishes or will of one or both of the parents; he has attempted to befriend the friendless without success; he finds himself used in sundry fashion; he has noted the controlling power exerted by one of his parishioners over another, as in illness. I saw a case recently wherein religion and God himself, were invoked as arbitrary controls exerted by a mother over a teen-ager trying to flap independent wings. Mother subtly used the whiplash of eternal damnation to get her daughter "saved" from gaining independence of the mother's wishes (see p. 120).

In psychoanalytic language the quality of human relationships has been described popularly as "object relations."[8] "Object" here has no reference to people as things, but is used in contradistinction to "subject." Thus, the psychologically well-developed person will not deal with others as subjects of his own, extensions of himself, antitheses of himself, but as individuals independent of his own psychological makeup. The mature person knows his "ego boundaries," knows where he leaves off and others begin. In the case just cited, for example, this mother's ego boundaries were sufficiently indistinct that she could not see her daughter as a separate entity. There existed a partial psychological symbiosis which consequented in the teen-ager's fright of leaving the mother. Together with the mother's unconscious wish to keep her close, a "school phobia" developed. The patient was afraid, not of school, but of leaving her mother.

Much has been written about "object relations" but we are forced to give it only brief mention to suit the purposes of pastoral diagnostic

[8] Freud, "Instincts and Their Vicissitudes," op. cit., Vol. XIV, p. 109.

thinking. A characteristic of importance in well-developed or good object relations is the nature and quality of the love expressed in such a relationship. Here, theoretically and theologically the pastor can grab hold most easily. Psychoanalysts Michael Balint[9] and Erich Fromm[10] have made some attempt to examine the quality of loving. No theologian examines this question of object love more closely, philosophically, than Anders Nygren.[11] The capacities to share and exchange, to give and to take, to love and to be loved, to respect others as one can respect himself, are common sense qualifications of good object relations. "Closeness" did not formerly have to be qualified as a positive quality, but nowadays the character of the closeness needs examination, as witness the "closeness" of the mother and daughter cited above.

Mechanisms of defense. Since our intent is descriptive we offer but a flavor of those repetitious patterns of the self that protect against psychological pain through illustrations of such mechanisms. A woman parishioner hears the pastor in public prayer asking earnestly for forgiveness. She has been struggling unbeknownst to herself with fears of sexual promiscuity, and assumes that the minister's diligent prayer is offered so earnestly because *he* (not she) is such a sinner in the flesh. This unrecognized irresponsibility for her own feelings is called "projection." Not infrequently at the bed of the dying the minister may witness in the patient as well as in the relatives the mechanism of "denial" which puts aside the fact of imminent death. Unprovoked attacks by a teacher on her Sunday School class of boys may be recognized by the pastor as a "displacement" of her wrath from an errant husband to more helpless male representatives.

Freud anticipated the concepts of mental mechanisms of the ego, but their elaboration was described by his daughter, Anna. Her work helped clarify the mind's methods for keeping the peace.[12]

[9] *Primary Love and Psychoanalytic Technique* (London: Hogarth Press, 1952).
[10] *The Art of Loving* (New York: Harper & Row, Publishers, 1956).
[11] *Agape and Eros* (Philadelphia: The Westminster Press, 1953).
[12] Anna Freud, *The Ego and the Mechanisms of Defense* (New York: International U. Press, 1946).

It does not seem appropriate that the pastor know in detail the intricacies of the mechanisms of defense which serve as buttresses against the anxiety aroused by intrusion of primitive impulses into consciousness. It may be of value to point out, however, that a routine part of a psychiatrist's responsibility is not only to ferret out those mechanisms of defense his patient is using qualitatively, but quantitatively as well. He will make some judgment as to the strength of his patient's psychological makeup on this basis. It is also important for the pastor to know that these mechanisms are vitally important to the smooth functioning of the personality, to be more respected than attacked. For example, with the dying patient who has made it plain that he is not about to deal with his own death as a reality, ministers' or doctors' efforts to overcome this defense meet with closed ears, enragement, or estrangement. Though unlikely but certainly a danger, an anxiety attack may be the consequence of ramming home the facts. Attacking defenses has long been out of vogue in effective psychotherapeutic technique, though the value of assessing defenses diagnostically remains. Since the operation of all mechanisms of defense are unconscious, it never behooves the minister to jump with hobnail boots into the precisely interdigitated cogwheels of the mind that are the psyche's defense against discomfort, anxiety, and panic.

Capacity to learn intellectually and emotionally. Native intelligence is considered to be a "given" that arrives with the newborn as ready for development as his musculature. It is not an uncommon experience, however, for clinical psychologists to find considerable difference between an individual's latent intelligence quotient and his functioning quotient. The differences at times are minimal. But, at others, they are dramatic to the degree that a child who appears to be dull may have an intellectual capacity in the normal or even bright-normal range. The difference between these intelligence measures is usually accounted for by some interference in the learning process and most often attributable to the deflection of energies into conflicts away from the work and pleasure of attention, perception, and integration.

But the minister does not go around with the Wechsler-Bellevue test in his hip pocket. Without it he may, nevertheless, make useful assessments of his parishioners, particularly children and adolescents. He may recognize a discrepancy in the intellectual capacity shown by a youngster in school or church performance from that which his parents expect of him or which he actually may show at home. The minister may play a helpful role in those situations where bright children have dull or disturbed parents, and in the reverse situation wherein bright and perhaps overly expectant parents find it difficult to accept a retarded or even an average child. Alert pastors may be instrumental in preventing brilliance and creativity in their flock from going down the drain.

The capacity to "profit by one's experience" is a reflection of a strength of the inner self. Although the pastor is not equipped to measure such capacities, when he sniffs out vast differences in what is done by and what is expected from a youngster, he may early be of great service by helping his young parishioner and perhaps his family to appropriate sources of measurement and examination.

Capacity for tolerating life stresses. This particular ego strength has already been touched upon under "development." Much of the impetus given to the field of pastoral care came directly out of clinical settings where certain acknowledged stresses, e.g., illness, were obvious. It is the rare minister now that does not have at least an idea that there is required of him a somewhat different quality of assistance in his ministry to the sick, the dying, the bereaved, the prisoner, the serviceman, the maritally conflicted, and the troubled counselee.

The usual problems of stress wherein a minister's services have already been found useful have become so familiar for some members of the cloth as to be "old hat." In spite of the flood of interest in pastoral care for the men in obvious duress, the *subtle* stresses wherein ministers may be of special help seem to have for the most part escaped notice. The pastor's preventive potential especially in the field of mental health is almost entirely untapped when we leave the areas of the traditional concepts of stress. For example, problems arising out of marital infidelity gain immediate notice—but what about the problems of marital fidelity!

To raise such a question requires explanation. To ask other questions of similar character points equally directly at those areas of stress in parishioners' lives largely ignored by schools of pastoral care. Although proper attention has been paid to bereavement as a stress worthy of the clergyman's help, what about births? Retirement? Promotions? Weddings? Children's graduations, confirmations, bar mitzvahs? There has been too long a tacit assumption that these events in parishioners' lives are not only stress-free, but for the most part thought of as "happy" or deserving of congratulations. The point here is a simple one. From the standpoint of mental health these events for some parishioners may be more traumatic than war, sickness, catastrophe, death, or imprisonment. The eyes of pastoral care have been so focused on these latter "always-to-be-considered-stresses" that the horizon of pastoral help has been grossly limited to these well-demarcated anxiety precipitants. Although it is true that these events are often stressful, they are not *always* so and indeed may be anxiety alleviating for some individuals. A war or enemy outside, externalized, may be far easier tolerated than the enemy within.

The pastor, genuinely interested in the mental and spiritual health of his congregation, must have his eyes and ears diagnostically attuned to those events that his parishioners *perceive* as stressful. To raise the question about the stressful aspects of marital fidelity must not be construed as indictment of same. Divorce remains a great human tragedy and, historically, the Church has properly used its strength against it. However, when keeping a husband and wife together becomes an end in itself, it becomes easy to assume that when couples stay together the Church's responsibility and interest is ended. Ecclesiastically there is no problem? The suffering of the individuals goes on silently or is expressed in sufficiently devious ways that it may appear to the pastor intent on saving marriages that all is well. We do not consider the saying "People who pray together, stay together" a magical solution, though it does say something about communication. But does it follow that people who are forced by their church, pastor, or conscience to remain husband and wife will pray together because they stay together? The question that is raised here does not concern the morality of parishioners' problems of marriage, divorce, or infidelity. The moral question that *is* raised has to do with the responsibility of the Church toward its members' suffering, whatever its sources.

A characteristic of our "plant" that tells us of his strength is his capacity to handle stressful situations. This would, of course, imply some understanding on the part of the pastor of those factors that are peculiarly stressful to his parishioner. The Dutch Elm Bark Beetle is not likely to be troublesome to the city tree of St. Louis, the sycamore. This fungus-bearing insect will long be remembered, however, by the residents of Rockford, Illinois, where the shade and beauty of their city tree, the elm, are memories. It may take a little thought, some perceptive listening, and maybe even abandonment of portions of preconceived ideas of stress to learn what may be "bugging" a parishioner.

Capacity for expression of feelings. Another quality that characterizes the strength of the self is the range and appropriateness of the affective or feeling life. In patients ill with schizophrenia we see what is called a "flattening of affect." To the careful observer, this leveling of emotional range is not hidden or missed behind facial distortions that mimic different human feelings. For whatever reasons, these unfortunates seem to send out the tones of only one note in their human communications. Patients ill with this dread disease, stimulated by internal secrets and prohibitions, also sound inappropriate affective tones, such as laughing when they should be crying. We know that the schizophrenic is not without real feelings, he may just look that way. Other kinds of affective disturbance are seen in troubled persons who display continual sadness, suspiciousness, euphoria, guardedness, aloofness, fearfulness, or lability. The capacity for wide and appropriate affective expression is a reflection of strength in the ego or self. Healthy people are capable of sounding notes from the entire console of the affective organ. Their feelings run high and deep, they can share them, not become lost in them, take responsibility for them, and usually, like others around, appreciate them.

Degree of manifest emotional crippling. If we return for a moment to Freud's advancing army analogy and assume that everyone has a finite number of ergs of energy available for use in the business and pleasure of living, it becomes clear that every internal struggle reduces his "troops" for facing life's battles. The student who cannot apply himself, the wife overinvested in meticulous housework, the depressed, the diseased, the worried, the philanderer, the eater, the wanderer, the obsessed doubter, the trouble-maker are all burning up energies that take away from the tasks and pleasures at hand. The observant pastor can make some assessment not only of the quantity of energies lost by his parishioner from the daily task but can make some judgment about the quality of energies lost in neurotic discharge. In knowing his parishioner, he may be able to decide if the troops withdrawn from the front of everyday responsibilities are in a constructive retreat or not. For example, are they deployed in fighting illness or in the struggle of bereavement, or are they tied up in taxing neuroses like the drain on an auto's engine by spinning wheels hung in ice?

Capacity for testing reality. Differentiation of the self from other human beings has been discussed earlier. A fuzziness of ego boundaries offers a distorted perception of the world as most people see and experience it. The hallucination of the psychotic individual, for instance, is perceived as a voice external to himself instead of an inner experience. Hallucinations, delusions, and illusions are gross reality distortions and seldom escape discernment. But in this measurement of ego strengths, as with the rest already mentioned and those to be mentioned, there is a gradient. Phenomenologically, the capacity to test reality has been used to differentiate degrees of mental illness from the psychotic through the neurotic to the normal. Thus the healthier the ego, the greater is the capacity to differentiate with sharp and accurate perception what is real and what is unreal, what is self and what is nonself. In the psychotic individual there are characteristic distortions of reality. Since the defense mechanisms appear designed to preserve the comfort of a person rather than the clarity of perception of the real world, the latter may be subserved to protect against anxiety. One can preserve more esteem and comfort for oneself if one's thought is, "He hates me, and therefore my anger is justified," than to think, "I hate him without reason," or "because he attracts me."

In order to contrast neurotic from psychotic distortions of reality, I might cite the poet Byron. Born with a clubfoot, he was aware of his deformity, did not deny that he was physically different from most men, and was in this respect not bereft of his reality sense in psychotic proportions. But what he apparently could not see and did deny was that his deformity made any difference. His shaky uncertainty of his male identification demanded he prove to himself and others his masculine capacities. Consequently he gained the reputation as a lover who "fathered half of Europe" and in so doing safely guarded against the fright that he might be lacking in performance as a man. His pseudo-masculine world-view that made every woman a harem member permitted him to put aside personal dangers of enraged husbands, acceptance of responsibility for his woman partner, and/or offspring, his reputation, and his own guilt in order to preserve a persistent view of himself as a competent man.

Other examples of acute neurotic reality distortion are the cardiac neurotic who does not believe the competent examiner's verdict, "No heart disease"; the phobic whose fear goes unallayed by the operator's assurance, "This elevator's cables have triple reinforcement"; the depressed Nobel prize winner whose self-respect is unenhanced by a colleague's attempt to comfort him with, "You've won the world's acclaim."

The normally functioning individual is never totally free of reality distortion, either chronically or acutely. At the scene of an automobile accident the retinas of three observers from the exact same vantage point will have received the identical stimuli but what is "seen" and recalled by each may be completely contradictory, even if each is neutral. The degree of distortion and conviction, of course, is heightened if A's friend was the driver of the Chevrolet, B's of the Ford, and C is an automobile insurance executive of an involved company.

The concept of limited energies, referred to earlier, makes understandable how the world may be arranged to suit an individual's needs by the distribution of his developmental (troop) investments. On a family motor trip father, as driver, devotes his attention to the road; mother to direction signs, compass, the map, *and* the road; teenage daughter watches for the boys; hungry son concentrates on inn advertisements; and little brother's needs prompt him to search for service stations.

Each person's view of the world, his perception, and attention do not emanate from his immediate circumstances alone, but are influenced by his whole life experience including his early formative developmental years. "Where a man's treasure is, there will his heart be also" has a modern corollary in, "The eyes of business have dollar signs for pupils." Closer to home, when philosophical controversy over the nature of the universe reaches irrational proportions, one can be confident that each proponent's dogmatic views of reality are fed by his own early formative life experiences, his character, and his current interests. Small wonder the opponents "take things personally."

The pastor diagnostician will hopefully not only be equipped to differentiate the bizarre and serious reality distortions in his parishioner from those less pathological, but will begin to develop an appreciation for the innuendoes of his parishioners' world views as reflecting something of the believer's own person, his whole life experience contributions, his current needs, and his strengths and weaknesses.

Capacity for insight. There are many complicated definitions of insight but for our purposes we would define it simply as the capacity to see oneself as others do. This definition presents an immediate link to concepts just described. Insight is an element of reality testing applied to the self. To know where oneself, one's own wishes, hopes, ambitions, and problems end and another's begin, to know the difference between opinion, dogma, and fact, and to discern one's actual place in the world are qualities of insight.

In this definition of insight, humility in its *original* connotation approaches the quality of an ego strength. Humility has undergone a number of changes of meaning, however, and according to Webster "humble" now often connotes undue self-depreciation, sometimes verging on abjectness. This modern definition is no longer a quality of health or strength but a symptom of depression or a character trait of a person fearful of self-assertion or self-affirmation. In Christian circles, especially, to be humble approaches self-negation, bowing and scraping, and false positions of passivity which turn to the world for praise, not unlike those attitudes shown by "Uncle Toms," the integrationists' Quizlings. The old definition of humility, however, is to be "down to earth" not proud, haughty, or arrogant. Correct reality perception of the self would allow one to say "this is what I am and this is what I am not." Humility then, will not invoke pity, praise, reassurance or, most importantly, distancing.

At the other end of the insight scale would come those who see their role, their function, their behavior, and their personality as no one else does. The very depressed person may see himself as completely unworthy of help or attention from another, as the *world's* worst sinner. The paranoid claims the *world* persecutes him. He may take an equally psychotic position by placing overevaluation of his worth to the world in grandiose style. A highly narcissistic person will have carried through adulthood the mind of the infant whose world rotates about him as in his first few months of life.

One interesting quality of self-blindness or insightlessness appears paradoxical or even perhaps ironic. What strikes one as bothersome, irritating, offensive, or distasteful in another may be the very same attribute he does not see in himself. This applies not only to negative qualities but may apply also positively. In other words, what we like or dislike in others may offer a mirror to see oneself. Psychoanalysts begin their training with a personal analysis in an attempt to reduce blind spots and clear timbers from the eye.

Judgment. An accurate perception of reality offers maximum opportunity to make good judgments. When we speak of someone using "common sense" we indicate that he perceives the world and others the way most people do. Such a person reflects accuracy in perceptions, resulting in decisions that take the wishes and rights of others, as well as one's own, into consideration. When this particular quality of discernment and discretion is weak, the loss of "common sense" may stem from an injured brain or a disorder of the mind.

We would not have considered it good voting judgment in 1956 to have cast a ballot for Eisenhower *primarily* because he looked more like a father figure than Stevenson; it would be exercising similarly poor judgment for a delegate to the nominating convention of 1960 to have placed his vote in nomination for Kennedy over Stevenson to satisfy a neurotic wish to see a younger man win over an older one. Most cases of bad judgment occur because some internal disturbance brushes aside those aspects which may be of critical importance for the particular situation involved which, in this instance, would be the qualifications for office of the Presidency.

No parishioner, of course, uses persistently excellent judgment. The habitual absence of common sense should alert a pastor's concern, whether poor judgments occur in the religious, social, personal, or business life of the parishioner.

Life accomplishments and life equipment. It may be tempting to be critical of the parishioner who does not use his talents. But with most such people some disturbance of his mental health contributes. A great deal of astuteness is not required to recognize a parishioner who "fouls up" his life at all levels of his activities. We can be certain he is troubled. It requires more skill and sensitivity, however, to discern those making "an adequate adjustment," who are not in trouble with the law, have "respectability," but whose talents nevertheless are resting.

Although many citizens question that "man is created equal" socially, politically, religiously, or racially, there seems to be little doubt that men *are* unequal physically, intellectually, and emotionally. A question apropos of this particular ego strength is, "How is he doing under the circumstances?" The ability to use what one has been given profitably is a mark of emotional health. There is a vast degree of achievement difference between two car washers, one who is mentally deficient, and the other whose I.Q. is 140. While there is no doubt truth in "By their fruits ye shall know them," thinking of our "plant" and his strengths, we need also to consider "is the fruit produced of the quality and quantity one might expect from this particular tree?"

Other diagnostic vectors. The usefulness of the plant analogy comes to an end. Of the various vectors discussed up to this point each may play varying roles of importance in the consideration of the pastor's final assessment and conclusion. As noted earlier, if the pastor is overeager to help, he may well bypass important information that would permit him to make the most accurate pastoral diagnosis.

Three additional questions of basic importance to clarify a cloudy picture are, "What is the *trouble?*" "Why come to *me?*" "Why come *now?*" The physician never fails to deal with at least two of these questions in the form of "chief complaint" and "present illness." But since there are no diagnostic centers for human need, it often becomes appropriate for the physician as well to ask "Why me?" It appears to me that any person in a helping profession is likely to come to a useful "treatment plan" if all three of these questions get answered to his satisfaction. A lawyer in one of our seminars noted down the following exchange in his first interview with a client; it went like this:

LAWYER: "What brings you to see me?"

CLIENT: "I want a divorce."

LAWYER: "How did you happen to decide on coming to me?"

CLIENT: "You have a reputation for talking people out of getting divorces."

LAWYER: "Why do you want a divorce, now?"

CLIENT: "We got into a fight last week over whether I was flirtatious or not."

This tiny exchange took on huge meaning to the astute lawyer. Off to such a good start in knowing what his client said she wanted, really wanted, and how the trouble started and when, it was no surprise to learn he was able to help his client appropriately. Each of these three important elements in the diagnostic thinking of the pastor we will designate as: *the call for help, the call for help to the minister,* and *the call for help to the minister now.*

The call for help. Requests for assistance may or may not contain the answer to the question, "What is the trouble?" It would be slightly ridiculous to ask a parishioner what is troubling him when he has telephoned to let you know his mother just died or his house burned down or his wife was in an accident or his child is very ill. But if he calls "to chat," because "I haven't seen you in quite a while"; or asks that you "drop by when you're in the neighborhood"; or begins, "Remember that sermon a couple of months ago?"; it may take some detective work to learn what the trouble is. The call for help is frequently a major clue to diagnosis. It is surprising that so little attention is paid to it.

A complication here is that what is announced as the trouble may be a screen like a Halloween mask to children. The screen may hide the exact identity of the problem, but the very choice of a particular request itself may tell something about what is behind. The youngster's mask does not hide his eyes nor his voice nor his size. His aspirations, conflicts, character, or dreams may be played out in his costume and mask. Sometimes a "trick-or-treater" likes to unmask, but most do not like to have the mask removed by someone else even if he knows the adult knows who he is. There are some children for whom it is obviously better if the adult remains "mystified." The wise and considerate pastor will know that a parishioner who comes with a "mask" may be able to come only because he wears it. The pastor may even recognize the problem, begin work himself, or refer a person to the appropriate source of help without forcing the mask to be removed. A bank teller's complaint to one of our staff was an obsessive worry that "some of the funds are going to turn up missing, and I'll be held responsible." Although he did not recognize it, it was a thinly disguised wish and fear prompted by his wife's recent interest in the bank's president.

The call for help to the minister. Although the report of the Joint Commission on Mental Health indicates that over 40 percent of people troubled with emotional problems start with their minister, it is a missed opportunity if the pastor does not at some point learn why his parishioner or unknown client has looked *him* up. The minister soon comes to know which of his families view him as their first counselor about any matter of importance. For such families this particular facet of diagnostic concern may not be as useful as with others of his congregation or even strangers. What is diagnostically revealing about this particular question is not what the minister actually is or what the minister thinks he represents, but what this person before him thinks he is. In the case of the woman with marital difficulty, she did not seek out *any* lawyer. She sought out a lawyer "with a reputation for talking people out of divorces." In so doing the client revealed something of what she hoped to accomplish, namely, to be talked out of her interest in divorce. (In this particular situation the lawyer's reputation was real, not imagined; and it was specific.)

Generalizations regarding the character of men in the professions of law, medicine, and ministry are rarely assumed by individuals who may seek out a lawyer, doctor, or clergyman. Individual reputations may add a touch of reality to a parishioner's idea of what he can expect of his minister, but even when ministers are well known, grossly illogical and inappropriate expectations of them may occur. These illogical and, at times, peculiar appearing requests can sometimes be recognized as "transference" phenomena. The complicated constellation of meanings in regard to this concept developed by Freud must here be dealt with superficially and partially. It appears imperative that anyone in the helping professions should have at least an inkling of this phenomenon since one aspect of it appears to be universal. For our purposes, transference will be defined as any illogical unconscious response to another human being that stems from living history of early developmental years' experiences. What one person may expect from another then may be based not on the qualifications of the helper, but on the fantasied qualities transferred transiently from the characteristics of an early life figure or figures. Examples of transference, as defined, include: a husband who behaves toward his wife as if she were his mother; a wife who feels toward her husband as if he were her father; a businessman who treats his colleagues as if they were his own brothers; the rebellious private who views anyone with stripe or rank worthy of his contempt; the parishioner who sees any or all clergymen as his personal judge; the clergyman who expects special consideration from his bishop. These transference reactions occur spontaneously, are "built in," and are usually undetected and unrecognized. The immediate object of transference (in this case, the pastor), however, may recognize immediately that he is not what this person takes him for.

The importance of transference in our consideration is not that the pastor become expert in the laws, detection, or use of this universal "leftover" of childhood. (It is paradoxical that the only profession that has historically with some cognizance encouraged transference is the same profession that is forced to "relearn" its power. The constituents of no other profession have been called "father," "mother," "sister," or "brother.") What is important about the concept of transference to most pastors has nothing to do with the slowly developed and therapeutically powerful transferences that may be the lifeline of certain psychotherapies. We are focused, rather, on the effervescent immediate transference response with which the pastor must become familiar in his diagnostic horizons. He, like few others, offers the world, and especially parishioners, a figure loaded with potentiality for illogical response. Other loaded figures include policemen, movie stars, Presidents, drill sergeants, umpires and, contemporaneously, psychiatrists. Each of these has a potency for eliciting emotional representations of the past. The minister may notice his arrival brings changes in group behavior, household rearrangements, new conversational directions, and looks of surprise on the faces of strangers when, if not in clerical garb, his professional identity is revealed. Although he has learned to live with it and sometimes smile at it, all too rarely these reactions are misunderstood. (The young minister who repeatedly attempts to prove he is "only human" may succeed, but his effectiveness is doomed to failure.) Whether he likes it or not, and some ministers do not mind at all, the minister will be regarded as "special."

But someone may ask, "If ministers evoke such special reactions and there is not much a minister can do about changing such special reactions, why bother with it?" The answer is simple if, and only if, the minister is interested in *assessing* the person who comes for help and his needs. It may be tempting for a minister *not* to assess such reactions but simply bathe in them. More frequently than not, the office of the minister may evoke gain to the person of the minister either in the form of worldly goods or psychological supply. I first heard the "Jehovah Complex" described by Dr. Henry Schroeder, a revered professor at Washington University Medical School. He saw this complex as an affliction of physicians who come to look upon themselves as gods, reinforced by adoring transference reactions of their patients. The Jehovah Complex may not be specific to the profession of medicine. There are policemen who choose their jobs because they like the uniform's effects, drill sergeants because they need respect, movie stars because they love adulation, and ministers because they enjoy being special. But any one of these workers whose role evokes immediate transference reactions can, after a period, sift out differences in the initial response of others to him. The stimulus of his professional role he learns to separate from the stimulus of his person. This differentiation would be an impossible task if he were to be a drill sergeant one year, a pastor the next, a movie star the next, President the next, and so on. In his community the minister may notice that some people are attracted and others are driven away by his role, not his person. Once familiar with the potency of his station to others, the minister can enlarge his understanding of those who seek his help by using himself as a barometer. The minister learns to distinguish between himself and the image attributed to him by parishioners or strangers who seek him out.

The pastor gains insight into the immediate problem through the helpee's approach to him, in the call for help. What the parishioner hopes or expects the pastor will do or can do serves as a clue to the person's strengths to handle his problem.

One of the most common illogical responses to the role of the pastor is omnipotence or omniscience. Such a response, of course, has its normal place in the development of the small child who believes, "My daddy can do anything." In the child's world this may appear to be so. This expectation was preceded by an earlier time when *he* was able to command the environment to meet his infantile needs which were limited, intense, and when gratified, "ultimately" satisfying. Repetitions of these childhood hopes for the unlimited power and knowledge of other human beings may occur in adults, especially when under stress. A frantic husband grabbed our Billings' Hospital Chaplain's arm. He said, "Reverend, you've got to come and pray and bring my wife back. The doctors have pronounced her dead, but I know God wouldn't let a thing like that happen." The implication was, "by *your* power, as a man of God, you can bring her back."

The call for help, to the minister, now. Another element useful to diagnostic understanding is the *time* chosen for the approach of the parishioner to the pastor for help. "Why does he come now?"

Observant pastors have noted some peculiar human adjustments in their parishioners. They have seen husband and wife, whose relationship was obviously terrible, battle like cats and dogs for years and yet stay together without interest in help. They have seen individuals carry on in spite of fire, dungeon, and sword without a whimper. They have seen others racked with the pain of illness or loneliness manage their struggle with independence. There is hardly a parish without several long-sufferers who somehow perform the impossible. The economic energy concept reminds us that human resources are finite. Knowing the "precipitant" for seeking help now is most valuable in those situations where previously no quarter was asked. Although it may be difficult to ferret out the "last straw," it not infrequently is worth the effort because it may contribute to a sound helping plan.

A woman crippled by arthritis and confined for years to a wheelchair applied for psychiatric help, suffering with a mild depression. She had no relatives and lived alone. For years the pastor of her church, whoever it happened to be, had known the importance of weekly visits to Miss J. She apparently did not expect prolonged contact with the pastor. Her gratitude for the copy of the weekly worship service and church bulletin was of such magnitude that her then current pastor mistakenly felt these items were the important things. The day she received her first bulletin in the mail she began to get depressed. The cessation of the pastor's personal visits, brief as they were, was not the *cause* of her depression; but it became apparent that it was the precipitant.

When this now elderly woman was five years old, she and her mother were deserted by her father. She never married, partly out of her mistrust of men, protecting herself against the possible trauma of another desertion. Pastors had always been important to her as an ever-present reliable attentive man. When one pastor left, there was another to take his place in her life. The pastoral visits served the important function of guarding against being deserted again and allaying her consequent unresolved anger, initially directed toward her father who left her when she needed him most. Because of her father-transference to the pastor, *his* "deserting" her recapitulated her early trauma. With withering resources of energies, this "minor" incident precipitated her illness. It is important to note that the pastor did not *cause* her difficulties. This particular pastor recognized this without undue guilt and came to an appreciation of the intensity of importance attached to his pastoral role by her. A brief course of psychotherapy with a restitution of the old regime turned the tide, to put the outcome in an oversimplified way.

Looking for help may not come in the form of direct approach to the pastor but may be sought via behavior. For example, an "Easter-only" family that begins attending church regularly may be saying something in their action. An ordinarily dry-eyed communicant, welling tears with the wine, may wish to communicate more. "That sermon got to me" may not be simply a compliment to the pastor's preaching.

Religious data as a diagnostic vector. Pastors, particularly those interested in counseling, have long been aware that some parishioners use a religious topic as a vehicle to discuss something entirely different. Using a religious issue as a subterfuge behind which the parishioner *consciously* hides another issue is easily spotted by the sensitive pastor. Some ministerial counselors have insisted (correctly) there are not always other conscious problems lurking behind a parishioner's religious question raised in private.

Recent studies at the University of Chicago bear this out and go a step further (see page 115). This particular research has shown that religion itself may be a language of communication at several levels. There is not only a "religious problem" of import conveyed, but also the individual's religious ideas themselves may contain unconscious and, therefore, unseen concerns of the parishioner. This particular study showed that from religious ideas alone, elicited from patients in an interview structured to evoke only religious interests, activities, investments, and beliefs, a personality evaluation and clinical diagnosis can be accurately made. Furthermore, a patient's current psychological problems could be spotted in his individualized interpretations of religion no matter what his formal religious background happened to have been. The psychiatrists conducting the research, armed with their special tools of training, have demonstrated that the religion and philosophy of patients is an important part of them and not to be thrust aside, ignored, or eradicated. Also, religious convictions offer avenues to understanding the patient himself, as disclosing as any other personal facet of his life.

What this means in part is that as ministers become more skilled in psychological understanding, they may be able to permit themselves and their parishioners to use religious language again. It has become popular in pastoral counseling to "get down to cases," to deal with the "real" issues with parishioners, such as the problems of their sex life. Although there may be times that non-religious issues may take the fore in a counseling situation, as ministers become more astute in the meaning of the religious language used by their parishioners, there will be increasingly less need to avoid dealing with his parishioner and his problem in the framework of the religious.

A case vignette from this study will serve to illustrate the diagnostic capability of religious language to talk for the whole individual. A 23-year-old married woman had become obsessed with the fear that she might become a streetwalker. This fear engulfed much of her thinking and was her most prominent worry. In the interview devoted to religious inquiry, she revealed that her favorite and most important Bible character at that time was Mary Magdalene, "a woman most people didn't know was a prostitute." Her favorite Bible verse was, "Blessed are the pure in heart for they shall see God." The worst sin one could commit was "scandal; to tease a man who is not your husband and then turn him down." The most important religious act one could perform, she felt, was to "obey the laws of the Church. It's best when things are black and white and you don't have to rely on your own judgment but can be helped to control yourself by the Church's rules." Her favorite Bible story was, "Christ being pals with Mary Magdalene. It's strange people look upon Christ as a goody-goody, noble person. He really picked tax collectors and prostitutes, those who were loathed, to be interested in. If you want to imitate Christ, don't condemn people." The most religious concept to her at the time of her being interviewed was "immortality of the soul; if you're neither rewarded nor punished afterward, it makes no sense to subjugate the passions or be moral. I can put up with my pangs of conscience but if it means losing my soul, that's a different thing." Her idea of evil in the world was, "It's interesting. It gets here by clouded thinking. For instance, things might look good on the surface like going to bed with someone." Her idea of an after-life was, "it is to have the beatific vision—to see God." In short, it can be seen that various projective questions asked about one's current religious interests may be revealing in understanding not only one's religion, but one's person, as well. It was only for research purposes that religious ideas exclusively were sought. In practice, naturally, one does not so limit his investigation.

The various vectors of pastoral diagnosis mentioned so far have been oriented to the pastor's assessment of a single parishioner. The flavor of pastoral diagnosis may have its place in group assessment as well. Having practiced diagnostic thinking with individuals, the pastor may wish to employ similar principles in his assessment of other situations in his church from board business to prayer meetings. Diagnostic elements, e.g. those delineated in "Other Diagnostic Vectors," have direct applicability in the assessment of group problems. "What is this group asking?" "Why me?" and "Why now?"

Summary

Pastoral diagnosis is a term we have coined to describe elements that contribute to the assessment-decision-making responsibility of the pastor. Although it has its counterpart in medicine, psychiatry, and casework, pastoral diagnosis is uniquely clerical and is molded from the various vectors of human experience that are familiar to the pastor. The vectors we have described are indebted to and linked to the psychological understanding of personality. Our intent has been to call attention to the possibilities for a broadened perspective of the kinds of problems that may present themselves to pastors. No one vector we have described is adequate basis for a pastoral diagnosis.

Although mental health and morality are not mutually exclusive, they certainly are not to be equated. One of a group of pastors in a seminar recognized this distinction when he said, "I've liked this woman and I want to help her, but I've never been able to tolerate women who smoke. I'm trying awfully hard not to be troubled by it, but I must admit it alienates me. I give her all the characteristics, undeservedly, of a fallen woman. Not only that but, because she smokes, I think of her, I'm sure, as far more disturbed than she really is." This honest and frank confession opened the way, not only for this pastor, but for his entire discussion group to recognize something of the qualities of being "judgmental." One consequence of the discussion was a recognition that "bending over backwards" *not* to be judgmental of one particular act, habit, or attitude was already a harbinger of alienation from a parishioner. In the same discussion it was acknowledged that being "accepting" (for this group the opposite of "judgmental") was sometimes a distancing mechanism to avoid dealing with those problems of parishioners that were bothersome to the pastor, preventing him from coming to a judgment or decision. This particularly perceptive group also came upon the recognition that failure to come to some decision or pastoral diagnosis concerning a parishioner seldom served the pastor well. They perceived that "accepting everything" could be a false position, a pleasant way of rejecting someone, or an avoidance of dealing with one's own or the parishioner's hostile feelings.

Since the pastor cannot count on external agencies to assess the needs of his parishioners, he is sometimes forced to be a diagnostician. Lest we think for a moment we know what "needs" are, the usually clarifying Webster is likewise befogged. There are four definitions: "1) a condition requiring supply or relief; 2) the lack of anything requisite, desired or useful; 3) want or poverty"; and then he throws in the towel. Webster states a need is: 4) *"anything* needed or felt to be needed." Freud has pointed out, "An instinctual stimulus does not arise from the external world but from within the organism itself. An instinct never operates as a force giving a *momentary* impact but always a *constant* one. It impinges not from without but from within the organism. A better term for an instinctual stimulus is 'need.' What does away with a need is 'satisfaction.' "[13] Freud associated need with wishes and with psychological manifestations of the drives which he considered constitutional, ever present, demanding satisfaction. For

[13] Freud, *op. cit.,* Vol. 14, p. 118.

our purposes, we can say that a need is a persistent demand for gratification that is appreciated psychologically, but rooted in a man's constitution. The minister like any other diagnostician of human need, must learn something of what needs are and especially what needs his parishioners are presenting to him. He must decipher, not only *which* needs of the parishioner are crying out the loudest, but he must consider whether these crying needs can be satisfied by *him,* and if so, when? He must decide when the needs are not appropriately to be met by him, if they are to be met at all. If so, by whom? Finally, a subtle and difficult differentiation which the pastor must make is, *"Whose* needs are in the foreground?" A young man I encountered on a train had his own system for meeting the needs of alcoholics. To quote him, "I have to pass through skid row in Chicago on my way to work. These guys were always approaching me, and I knew if I gave them money just what they'd do with it. I got tired of being conned. What I do now is say, 'Are you really hungry?' and if they say, 'Yeah,' I march them off to the closest restaurant, sit them down and tell them to order. Then I pay the check and leave. They probably hated me." When asked how the system worked, especially since he never stayed to see the results of his "service," he said, "Well, you know, *now* when I walk down that street those guys leave me strictly alone. As far as I'm concerned, it's worked out fine and you can't tell—maybe I've helped somebody."(!)

It has become clear to the reader that he will look in vain in this section on pastoral diagnosis for psychiatric syndromes or a systematic review of psychopathology. Neither will he find delineation of those clinical signs or symptoms which direct him to refer a parishioner. The reasons are not because there is not room, nor because there are good texts already written[14] nor because the reader might not be interested or profit from such information. The reason is simple. The aim of this book is to stimulate pastors to enlarge their armamentarium of pastoral care for their people. Although reading, study, and train-

[14] Standard texts include: *Modern Clinical Psychiatry* by A. P. Noyes and L. C. Kolb (Philadelphia: W. B. Saunders Co., 1958); *Textbook of Psychiatry* by D. Henderson and I. R. C. Batchelor (New York: Oxford U. Press, 1962); *Dynamic Psychiatry* edited by F. Alexander and H. Ross (Chicago: U. of Chicago Press, 1952).

ing in a clinical setting are valuable, the development of working relationships with mental health professionals are far more enlightening. Ideally, psychiatric consultation should be as close as the pastor's telephone.

Various vectors in pastoral diagnosis cannot profitably be used as a checklist. In various situations some will have pertinence, others will be useless. Hopefully, they may serve as a reference and as a stimulus to a spirit of inquiry that will lend the pastor greater equipment in his decision-making with parishioners. Each pastor develops his own schema for diagnostic inquiry which, ideally, does not omit pertinent considerations for helpful decisions. Without diagnostic thinking, a pastor's treatment plans may become set into the same recommendations for each person and situation. Stereotypy should raise suspicions that he might be offering a patent medicine that cures everything. Commonly encountered formulae are: "Prayer changes things," or "If you start coming to church," or "You'll have to get back to confession," or "Tithing performs miracles," or "You need regular counseling sessions."

Each problem that presents itself to the pastor is a live one. Each has its own characteristics and uniqueness that requires all the skill, sensitivity, ingenuity, curiosity, and wish to help that can be mustered.

The following is a condensed version of a situation reflecting the spirit of pastoral diagnosis and treatment. A student minister received a written message from a middle-aged man and his wife two weeks after their marriage. The message read, "Visit soon—we're having trouble praying together." A rooming house address in the town was given. What the young pastor already knew about this couple included the following: both had been widowed and remained unmarried for a number of years; both came from respectable, simple, quiet farm homes; neither had lived in the larger community of 5,000; the man had been partially deaf for a number of years; a house they had hoped to have ready to move into after the wedding was not quite completed on the inside; each was pious and somewhat shy but during the wedding preparations both gave the impression of being in love and as excited as each could be; the man was some 10 or 15 years older than the woman and was mildly suspicious, not an un-common characteristic of people with hearing deficit. On the minis-ter's arrival at their one-room temporary quarters, several things be-came immediately obvious: any prayer above a whisper (or slight noise) could be heard in the hall or the room next door; a distant relative of the woman and two other church members lived in the same building; the wife did all the talking initially in low tones with her husband continually cupping his ear. The public nature of any conversation brought discomfort, not only to the couple, but also to the pastor; so the first move he made was to pile them into his auto and head for the local, and usually deserted, cemetery. Although the content of what was said to each other by this couple was important to them at the time, what was more important was that they were saying things to each other in decibels requiring no hearing aid. Neither the pastor nor the dead minded the verbal battle. After a while, completely on their own, they recognized that finished, or unfinished, they needed the privacy of their own home. After the pastor quickly sized up the situation, providing the means for re-opening channels of communication was the only pastoral treatment necessary.

CHAPTER THREE

PASTORAL TREATMENT

The initial considerations of pastoral diagnosis have set the stage for understanding our concept of pastoral treatment. As pastoral diagnosis is the pastor's decision regarding his parishioner's problem (consequent to his assessment of various diagnostic vectors), pastoral treatment is his ministerial plan for assistance in solving the problem. Pastoral diagnosis implies that a clergyman evaluates and concludes something. Pastoral treatment implies he *does* something. It becomes apparent that such a plan will be to some degree unique, not only because parishioners' problems reflect individual parishioners and circumstances, but also because each pastor will bring his own armamentarium of help. Treatment is defined medically as, "the management and care of a patient or the combatting of his disorder."[1] The clergyman has, as his charge, the pastoral management and care of a parishioner or joining the parishioner in combatting his disorder. Of course, the usefulness of pastoral diagnosis is completely obviated if the pastor has but one *frozen* plan for each parishioner, even if that plan's object has, as its lofty goal, salvation of a sinner.

Speaking broadly, we would not be averse to identifying our concepts of pastoral treatment with "pastoral care" except in two respects. First, if there was ever need for a "necessary" marriage, it is between diagnosis and treatment. Pastoral care, unwedded to husbanding principles of diagnosis, must contend with abortion and illegitimacy.

The fruits of labor won through pastoral action are far more likely to mature when they are conceived by appropriate plan rather than

[1] Dorland, *op. cit.*, p. 1, 540.

by the impulse to help. The pastor's plan of action, as with his diagnostic assessment is not mechanically executed. It is always implemented with contributions from his emotions or feelings. Depending on the circumstances, the treatment need not be arrived at only after prolonged, cold deliberation that smacks of isolation, but may be implemented immediately, not shorn of spontaneity. On the other hand, his treatment may be the act of waiting or even doing nothing. It is consequent to diagnostic decision. It is his consciously enacted response to the parishioner and his problem. Our intent, therefore, is to use deliberately the term "pastoral treatment" rather than "pastoral care" because the latter has not been linked nearly so closely to prerequisite evaluation processes.

Further, we see "pastoral care" chained and constricted to rather narrow concepts of assistance, e.g. pastoral counseling as the primary prescription. As ecclesiastical concepts of stress have been limited in scope diagnostically (see page 52), rather naturally, the treatment potential for pastoral care suffers compression. Pastoral care reaches farther than counseling the troubled, visiting the sick, comforting the dying, soothing the mentally disturbed, serving the imprisoned, or assisting the distressed. Pastoral care encompasses these activities and much more.

It is a movement dedicated to win back human affects for religion and to make religion serve the whole man, the heart of man. Therefore, it comes as no surprise that the leaders of this movement have been closely allied with the modern students of man's mind and affects, the psychologists, psychiatrists, and psychoanalysts. Of interest is the fact that the term "heart" is one of the most frequently used expressions in the Bible. Cruden's *Concordance* defines heart as follows: "The word heart is used in Scripture as the seat of life or strength; hence it means, mind, soul, spirit, or one's entire emotional nature and understanding."[2]

We envision the pastor of the future to be, not an expert in counseling, but an integrative force in the lives of his people and community, a priest in the religion of the heart. Because "pastoral care"

[2] Alexander Cruden, *Complete Concordance to the Old and New Testaments* (Philadelphia, Pa.: Universal Book & Bible House, 1930).

has become, unfortunately, a term constricted to certain pastoral actions, e.g. counseling (important as that act is), we prefer to use "pastoral treatment"—the total professional armamentarium of religions' representatives.[3]

The particular modes of pastoral treatment to which we will address ourselves are: pastoral counseling, referral, consultation, fees, and religion as a human resource.

Pastoral Counseling

The importance of counseling to the pastor or rabbi need not be justified as a pivotal mode of pastoral treatment. It is a modern development, grown like Topsy, with roots sunk deep in religious beginnings. If it wished to, the Church could place first claim, historically, to "spiritual treatment" and look with toleration at the "Johnny-come-lately" psychotherapists' "squatters' rights" to treat the soul. In partial response to modern psychology, the last 20 years have seen a fantastic growth of interest by the clergy in doing counseling. The minister has learned he not only has a right to counsel his parishioners, but an obligation. Some ministers and theologians, of course, question the usefulness and validity of counseling as a specialty. Others feel unsuited, disinterested, or uncomfortable doing it. For the most part the leaders of this new realm of pastoral care have been enthusiastic and pleased with their contribution. They see themselves in the field of counseling, justifiably, as positive forces working toward spiritual growth for counselees and as vital contributors to a community's mental health.

This special interest in counseling has not only become popular, it has outgrown the fad stage to become established in theological curricula. (Some consider this an ominous development.) The pioneering efforts of people like Boisen, Cabot, Dicks, Godin, Hiltner, Johnson, Oates, Westberg, and Wise have won a very important battle: the arousal of interest in pastoral care and especially one phase of it—counseling. But when the honeymoon for pastoral psychology is

[3] See Russell Dicks' book, *Principles and Practices of Pastoral Care* in this series.

over, will there be a marriage between its theology and its practice? Between ideas and implementation? Between scholarship and service?

In our observation, professors of pastoral care and psychology in the seminaries have had overwhelming responsibilities. Not only have they had to convince students of the important place of pastoral care in the work of the Church, but they have had to convince their scholarly colleagues in the secular and theological worlds as well. To maintain peer respect, therefore, if they are to be caught short on anything, it will not be scholarship. Pastoral psychology and care offer challenges that invite theological integrations with psychological theories and research gaps that stimulate their students to head for their carrels in the stacks. Besides functioning often as the seminary counselor, officially or unofficially, these professors of pastoral care must provide leadership and scholarly supervision at graduate levels. As keen and conscientious as I have found most of these seminary professors to be, they find there is simply not enough time for appropriate supervision at the operational or clinical level. The training offered by the Council for Clinical Training and the Institute of Pastoral Care, though crucial at the beginning and better by far than offering no clinical experience now, has not acquired sibling stature in the secular world of therapeutic psychology. *Perhaps* the current available training for ministers is suitable if one is to be a "general minister," who gives occasional counsel. But is it adequate for anyone who calls himself a counselor (whether the qualifying adjective before the latter is "pastoral," "marital," "premarital," or is absent)?

Raising this question gives opportunity to state my intent. It is not to blanket the subject of pastoral counseling with comprehensive coverage. Rather I intend to deal with certain aspects and issues that I consider to be of crucial importance in this expanding specialty of the ministry.

Should pastoral counseling be called and function as a "specialty" of the ministry? Is it, like church music or religious education, a field of interest familiar to most practicing pastors and a specific vocation of the few? The top specialists in religious education bring the finest aspects of the discipline of secular education to bear on the Church's scholastic problems. The minister of music does the same with the world's best training in music—which is available to him. How well these men function is of vital interest to their church but not necessarily to the worlds of education and music. It is different with the pastoral counselor in at least one major respect. How well *he* functions *is* a matter of concern to the community's interests and to professionals in mental health. The latter group has largely ignored the growth of this ministerial activity until recent years, but the impact on the public has now registered: the pastor sees himself and has come to be acknowledged by the laity, at least, as a resource person in community mental health. With the honeymoon of pastoral counseling drawing to a close, the mental health professional is asking a few basic questions of this specialty of the ministry: (1) How does pastoral counseling differ from psychotherapy? (2) If there are differences, are these simply nominal, hiding therapeutic maneuvers behind the aegis of religion? (3) If differences are real, what are the specific contributions to be made by the pastoral counselor? (4) If differences are nominal, does the training for the pastoral counselor meet secular psychotherapeutic standards? (5) What are the qualifications for a recognized pastoral counselor, and do these reflect the training background or experience that carries weight in the psychological helping professions? The psychiatrist is less interested in the theologically pertinent questions that ask, "Where should a pastor counsel?" or "Under whose auspices?" or "How does religion enter the counseling situation?" than he is in the questions, "What training experience and theoretical orientation is brought to bear on the counselee?" and "What goals are to be accomplished with parishioners?" and "Who supervises?" These are a few of the questions facing the maturation years of pastoral counseling.

This chapter could be written much more easily if it did not demand that definitions of psychotherapy and pastoral counseling be attempted. Although fogginess persists with these concepts there have been excellent definitions of each attempted by others. The charge this work must accept requires a definition that may lend a helping hand in answering some of the basic questions cited above. These definitions are offered, then, to point-up and sharpen the issues, not to soften them nor to delineate who should do what. Further, the definitional context is purely psychological, not theological.

The word "psychotherapy" has come to be a term so commonly

used with different connotations and loaded with pseudo-distinctive meanings that it is tempting to wish for its demise as a communicative word. But we are stuck with it. For our purposes "psychotherapy" is a formal arrangement between two parties (helper and helpee) who consciously consent to address themselves in communications, verbal and nonverbal, to effect—through psychological change—solutions to the problems presented.

A "psychotherapeutic maneuver" is a technique of a therapist designed to bring about a psychological effect that benefits the recipient whether the latter enters a conscious contract or not. While "therapeutic results" may stem from psychotherapy or a psychotherapeutic maneuver, they may result from any of the entire gamut of human events or interchanges and need not be tied in any form to a conscious formal contract between the designated healer and his subject. For example, a woman with a hysterical paralysis might be relieved of her symptom by a trip to Lourdes or down the sawdust trail to the altar of a healing evangelist with the direction of the trip prompted by her religious orientation. The same patient might be made ambulatory by a physician's "psychological maneuver" through a "powerful" placebo. Or she could get an equally rehabilitative result through hypnotherapy. All three of these approaches can abrogate the symptom without necessarily altering the internal conflicts which brought it about.

Before we define pastoral counseling, several rather important observations about the definitions above must be made. First, there has been no delineation of professional role in them. Second, there has been no judgment made in regard to the correlation of efficacy with training, skill, experience, or theoretical orientation. Thus, a shaman could qualify as a "psychotherapist" and a witch doctor as an agent using a "psychotherapeutic maneuver." Religion or even life's fortunate vicissitudes may offer "psychotherapeutic results." These omissions in the definitions are by no means intended to undercut the importance of training, skill, experience, or theoretical orientation—but rather to emphasize them. Theory and technique of pastoral counselors must be dissected away from questions like, "Where does psychotherapy begin and pastoral counseling end?" "If you do psychotherapy in the shadow of the Church's structure, is that pastoral counseling?" "If you counsel wearing a clerical collar should you expect religious or psychotherapeutic results?" "If you leave the unconscious mind alone and deal only with conscious expressions or religious ideas, isn't this counseling?" "Is listening, giving advice, or talking in religious terms psychotherapy if you don't make deep interpretations?" "If you don't see someone regularly for specified times, or see them only a few times, is that psychotherapy?"

In juxtaposition to the definition given above, pastoral counseling must be considered as a form of psychotherapy in which the therapist is a pastor. Although models, methods, training, accoutrements, skills, theories, and goals may be different, our definition of psychotherapy includes him along with the psychoanalyst, psychiatrist, case worker, physician, psychologist, shaman, and quack. How good or qualified or skilled or capable a psychotherapist is forms a different though *crucial* question. Further, if we continue to restrict ourselves here to psychological dimensions, there are techniques and actions of pastors that must be considered as "psychotherapeutic maneuvers." Taking the hand of a critically ill person, reading scripture, offering prayer, performing the priestly role, etc.—whatever their religious impact or the interpretation of such impact, psychological principles are at work as well!

An intended provocation that these definitions offer is the challenge to pastoral counselors to ask not, "Am I a counselor or a psychotherapist?" but "What *kind* of a psychotherapist am I and what techniques, skills, knowledge, and accoutrements do I require as a contributive helper to people in trouble?" Besides this provocative intent, however, there is an underlying functional principle that prompts these definitions—the principle of transference.

The subject of transference in pastoral care is worthy of a book in itself. From our point of view, it is a basic concept which sometimes gets lost in discussions that begin with questions like, "How far does the minister go in counseling?" or "Where does pastoral counseling leave off and psychotherapy begin?" The same kind of questions faced psychiatric caseworkers some years ago and eventually revolved in part around the issues concerning the development, visualization, utilization, and interpretation of transference (see page 62). Although the caseworkers have not yet as a body come to a completely comfortable solution in regard to interpretation of transference in psychotherapy, they have recognized the necessity for its respect.

In discussing this term earlier we focused attention largely upon the phenomenon of transient illogical responses of parishioners to ministers in a pastoral situation. Although important, these "transference reactions" are sporadic and of an intensity little different from other "transference figures" cited earlier. But in the casework and pastoral counseling (psychotherapeutic) situations the nature and intensity of transference is of a different order.

It is pretensive for a therapist, regardless of what his professional monicker is, to assert that he is not a psychotherapist because he "leaves the unconscious alone and deals only with the conscious." This is especially presumptuous when there may be sore inadequacies in his recognition of the differences between the two in the therapeutic situation. There pervades the bland assumption in pastoral counseling that the pastor will "remain himself," especially if he uses a technique such as "Rogerian" which does not ask questions, or "probe" or permit the therapist to "get ahead or behind" the parishioner. Any therapist, whatever his profession, who sees a person regularly over a period of time will begin to wear a powerful mantle he does not own, placed there invisibly by his subject. The greater the number of hours logged in a one-to-one situation, *no matter how it may be structured by the therapist,* the greater will be the development and intensity of the transference. Rogerian psychology and techniques have been marvelously instructive and perhaps continue to be a useful beginning orientation for pastoral counseling. But for protracted counseling, its usefulness disintegrates primarily for one reason—visualization of the phenomenon of transference is obscured and unheeded.

Without redefining transference but rather translating it into a functional example, a parishioner's transference towards his pastor might be expressed as follows, "Although the facts are that you are not my father (mother, brother, sister, grandfather), the feelings and attitudes that you evoke in me without my awareness are of the same character and strength toward you as they were toward him when I was a child."

There are degrees of intensity and variation of quality in transference. Although there seem to be some correlations of intensity of transference with exposure time to the transference figure, there are parishioners who without a previous contact develop an immediate intense transference reaction with a first meeting. (Some criminals, for instance, regard all policemen as punitive, destructive enemies who serve as external representations of an internalized hated parent.) In general, and with some exceptions, the psychologically developed or mature personality is less likely to experience overwhelming transference reactions with a first meeting. The more adult reaction is a discriminating one that does not make all pastors into psychological fathers (or mothers). The easiest avenues of detection wherein a pastor can recognize that he is made into a figure of the past existing in the parishioner's mind is in the affective (feeling) and behavioral realm. Transference is usually more difficult to recognize in ideation and verbalization.

Intensity of transference to the pastor may vary with personality maturation of the parishioner but may also be related to the *office* of the pastor as well, reflected by reactions he evokes in the many, not the few. The variations here may range from a mild filial reaction to grossly exaggerated expressions that can reach psychotic proportions. Pastors cannot miss the latter whether these psychotic transferences take the form of erotomania, paranoia, or an infantile dependency in submissive quality not unlike the imprinted gosling that follows a laboratory technician as its "mother."

But these gross distortions by parishioners are unusual. In my experience with a few pastors, I find their discrimination of parishioner transferences is limited to vague awareness that something peculiar is going on. Others are aware of positive or negative reactions of parishioners to them which seem inappropriate. Some continue counseling a parishioner until adverse currents are encountered on the one hand, or until positive infantile feelings get out of hand on the other.

The pastor like the physician is a sitting duck for transference reactions. The minister learns, for instance, whether he has attributed the phenomenon to transference or not, that the moon-eyed teen-age girl who dotes on him is using him somehow like a shadow representative of another man. He could callously derogate her reaction to "a phase" or mistake it for budding adult love. If he has learned to take these crushes seriously, but not too seriously, he may handle it with sensitivity and objectivity. Doing the latter he has, without conscious intent, acknowledged the strength and importance of a steaming transference reaction. As many attitudes toward or conceptions of parents that children have constitute the number of possible transferences toward the pastor.

Transference is the current lively reenactment of childhood feelings to childhood figures, recapitulated in the present. Since no parent-child relationship is 100 percent univalent, there will be periods of positive and negative feelings experienced by the patient toward the most skillful of therapists in any extended psychotherapy wherein the goal aims beyond symptom relief, e.g. in psychoanalysis.

The counseling situation may stimulate a transference reaction which in itself leads to a psychotherapeutic result of varying duration. For example, a counselee's internal resources are suddenly strengthened, he conquers his manifest problem, and leaves treatment thinking the counselor to be an unusually superior human being. In my supervising experience, a number of "marvelous miracles" worked by therapists within one to five interviews, when subjected to scrutiny, became less miraculous but no less marvelous "transference cures." Similarly, patients taking "flight into health" are amazing to behold and on the surface appear transformed. The therapist "responsible" for participating in these problem solving adaptations may not know anything of transference in order for these phenomena to occur. The sincere minister who is willing to lend a helping hand will occasionally experience an unusual privilege. Whether he might be psychologically unsophisticated or not, he will witness people get up off the floor of adversity through turning to him for strength he did not know he possessed. Although these results cannot be called the handiwork of skilled psychotherapists, their importance cannot be overstated for the individual benefited nor for the potent role of the figure of the man of the cloth. But by bestowing all such experiences to the "grace of God," without curiosity and examination, the student of pastoral diagnosis misses as rich an opportunity for learning as he would if he attributed hallucinations to the "voice of the devil."

In my experience with pastors, I find they are eager to seek clarification in their daily work of those irrational reactions expressed in their direction. Because they are interested in motives for behavior, they usually take these transference reactions in stride. But the transference developed in the counseling situation is still mysterious and its intensity nearly unbelievable to them. I am reminded of one of my own eye-opening experiences as a beginning resident psychiatrist. I had been treating a 15-year-old girl for about a month when I was asked to present her case in a child therapy seminar to my admired teacher, Dr. Othilda Krug. The patient had come for four visits. After the initial greeting, each session presented lengthy silences punctuated only with questions of mine which evoked answers of the "yes" and "no" variety. Her spontaneous communications were nil. She occasionally stole glances at me. I was pleased, in a way, to present the case because I felt frustrated, uncomfortable with her shy silences, and plagued with the thought, "Nothing's going on with this girl." On the other hand, I was distressed about the presentation itself. I knew her background problems and history as reported by others, but what was there to report about her treatment? Pressured by this gaping deficiency, I, in mild desperation, asked her if she ever had any dreams. To my shock she reported that after her first visit to see me, she had been dreaming regularly with a number of dreams about the treatment situation! She had not reported these "because I didn't know you were interested." To my eyes that did not see, she looked uninvolved. I had missed completely her rapidly developed paternal transference.

Sophisticated psychotherapists have acknowledged the centrality of transference as the cutting edge in intensive psychotherapy or analysis since Freud's original contributions.[4] By this phenomenal expression of the unconscious mind the patient permits one foot to

[4] Freud, "Interpretation of Dreams," op. cit., Vol. V.

wander by regression back into his infantile past keeping the other solidly planted in his adult present. Under these conditions the patient's observing powers, with the aid of his interpretive ally, the therapist, achieve the prized goal of intensive psychotherapy—insight. To appreciate and use therapeutically specific transference manifestations requires years of training and intensive supervision. We expect our graduating psychiatric residents to have acquired treatment skill that goes beyond recognition only, of transference phenomena in their patients.

Although such skill is well out of range of a pastor's needs or expectations, learning something of the nature, power, and characteristics of transference is not. For whatever reasons, as of now, it is a subject known to ministers more by intuition than by study.

A medical student attempting psychotherapy is often relieved and enlightened to learn he did not "do anything" that evoked a startling reaction of a transference nature in his patient. The surprising realization that an illogical attitude, thought, or action expressed toward him in the treatment situation was an inappropriate outbreak of a patient's childhood feelings freed up the student's objectivity and widened his treatment latitude. We expect well-trained student caseworkers, our senior medical students, and psychology interns to have had a theoretical grounding and a supervised live encounter in a clinical experience with this childhood leftover in adult lives. It is my conviction that the well-trained pastor of the future will be at least equally equipped.

Transference is a fascinating subject, crucial in psychotherapy. I hope that this glimmer of it and the problems it presents will stimulate the searching minister to find appropriate sources of reading, observation, and supervision that expand his appreciation of this universal and peculiar internal preservation of our tiny days. There are numerous theoretical and practical questions that concepts of transference present to pastoral counseling. A few of these are: "Will knowledge of transference further or blight a minister's efficiency?" "How experienced should a pastor be in transference issues?" "Is it always present between therapist and patient? pastor and parishioner?" "Where does it leave off and mature relations begin?" "Is basic trust or faith a transference phenomenon?" "How can one be sure illogical responses of parishioners are not logical ones inspired by the stimuli of a pastor's or therapist's unrecognized counter-transference?" (see p. 96) "How do the encounters of the parishioner with the pastor outside the counseling situation influence the latter? And does it matter?"

There are a number of types of psychotherapy even in the psychodynamic schools.[5] The skilled psychotherapist will make an appropriate diagnostic assessment to determine which approach is likely to be most efficacious. Whichever he decides to employ, an important aspect of his treatment in *any* type will be a continuous assessment of the patient's transference.

Although all skilled psychotherapists are more at home with certain types of psychotherapy than others, hopefully their training will permit them access to a repertoire of approaches. Supportive and suppressive psychotherapeutic skills are basic to physicians in the general practice of psychiatry. Contrary to some contemporary mythology, psychiatrists *do* say things besides "Uh-huh" and "What do you mean by that?" Passivity cannot be permitted to masquerade as "permissiveness." It may even be shocking to note that under certain circumstances and with certain patients psychiatrists may behave with authoritarian vigor! Their diagnostic assessment may require that they tell a patient to "Shut up" or "Cut that out!"

Another dying myth is that psychiatrists invite patients to unbridle their instincts. With certain patients pursuit of the motivation for behavior may be therapeutically preferable to its suppression. But I know of no psychiatrists of quality who characteristically tell their patients, "Have an affair" or "Why don't you try masturbation?" Patients with a weakened ego or a "holey," perverse, or sadistic conscience may turn to authority figures for help in controlling their impulses or drives. The authority may be the police, psychiatrist, or pastor. For such patients an "accepting" attitude may be completely

[5] See Chapter 11 "Principles of Psychiatric Treatment" by Dr. Maurice Levine in *Dynamic Psychiatry*, Franz Alexander, M.D. and Helen Ross, editors (Chicago: University of Chicago Press, 1952).

unsettling if it offers an invitation to liberation to proscribed drives instead of control. Thus, an authoritarian priest, rabbi, minister, and/or authoritarian religion is a necessary external control for some people. "Sanctuary!" may be sought out by the patient whose drives are on the loose. The discerning, capable psychiatrist will have made a diagnostic appraisal of such patients that requires him to be direct, suppressive, or authoritarian in support of the struggling ego.

These observations are intended (1) to undercut the pervasive tendency of pastoral counselors to consider passivity and acceptance as eternal virtues; (2) to indicate the necessity for assessment before response; (3) to hint at the possibilities for "supportive" treatment that are not limited to permissiveness, expressed solicitude, sympathy, acceptance, toleration, or hand-holding.

It becomes understandable why some psychiatrists are unimpressed with the counselor who disclaims the psychotherapeutic role with something like "I only offer supportive help," when the nature of what might be truly supportive to the ego of a struggling client, parishioner, or patient is unknown to him. "Supportive psychotherapy" has been undeservedly denigrated and stripped of its respect. It has been inappropriately delegated to the unskilled therapist primarily because of misconceptions. Our first-year resident psychiatrists, for instance, commonly come to training to learn the "real" treatment, i.e. "insight," "intensive," "psychoanalytic," or "uncovering" psychotherapy. Their common experience is to appreciate the skill, effectiveness, and difficulty of supportive therapy only after two or three years of training and supervision. In at least one respect, intensive psychotherapy may be easier for therapists in training—the transference is more discernible from session to session when appointments are closely spaced in time.

There is an impressive segment (42 percent) of people with emotional problems who begin their search for help with pastors. There are overwhelming numbers of hours invested in pastoral counseling (therapy by our definition) by ministers as compared with the relatively paltry number of all psychiatrists across the nation. In spite of these facts, very little interest or effort on the part of psychiatrists has been mobilized as yet to do *anything* constructive about the pastor's dilemma. Some express an ostrich-like "maybe-they-will-go-away" if the "stop-them" attitude is not adhered to. Encouraging notes have been sounded in the current rise in popularity of social psychiatry. More professionals have become interested in community psychiatry. Recognition of the potential of the physician, nurse, teacher, and pastor as useful agents in this service on the local scene is taking place.

It might be tempting for a clergyman to blame psychiatrists for the responsibility of interdisciplinary isolation. However, it appears that any real progress that will bring pastoral counseling into the status of a vital force in community mental health may initially require its impetus from the clergy.

If I were forced to choose a single factor now missing that would give me pause to predict a full-flowering contribution by pastoral theology and care, it would be a supervisory system of stature. Such a system needs to be constructed not only for the specialist in pastoral counseling but for the general practitioner of pastoral care as well. In any training program for those who specialize in intra-personal therapies, supervision is a *sine qua non*. Up to the present, standards of supervision in the Church have been geared not to *inter*-professional but *intra*-professional standards. The Church has considered expert supervision not as a "without which nothing" but as a "without which something." It is no accident that referral activities are a one-way street from the pastor to some other professional. This is by and large *not* because the other professional does not feel religion or the Church may not be of great benefit to his client or patient. It is partly because he cannot rely on the minister's professional qualifications for counseling or suitable care along psychological lines. The only sound basis such a professional has, up to now, for referral to the cleric is his firsthand knowledge of the pastor in his person or past work.

My conviction is a simple one. Pastors who devote a large proportion of their time to counseling owe it to themselves and certainly to their parishioners to have had a training which gives them sufficient knowledge and skill to allow them to do more good than harm. As of this time there is neither legal nor *any* inter-professional standards.

constructed for pastors doing counseling as their primary task. If the pastoral counselor is to take advantage of contributions and the understanding of man psychologically, training and supervisory experience must be made available to him or he must build towards providing them himself. It is my belief that the current available training for ministers is suitable at best only if he is to be a "general minister." If he is to do counseling but rarely, clinical exposures offered in pastoral training programs may be adequate; but it is simply no longer adequate for the pastor whose primary activity in pastoral care is counseling.

It is apparent that a large number of ministers must of pastoral necessity do counseling. This seems no argument against an insistence that those few specialists that do it routinely know exactly what they are about. Perhaps the majority of pastors fall between these two groups. Uncertainty troubles these pastors who keep encountering their own nagging questions, "Am I supposed to be doing this, and if so, am I doing it well?" Why not have the best training and ongoing supervision available that not only allows these men to be helpful, but which also presents them with the opportunity to enhance their self-esteem and confidence and to sharpen their growing edge? A little knowledge need not be a dangerous thing if it is appropriately utilized and helps one to avoid inappropriate enlistment of powerful psychological armamentarium.

The birth of the American Association of Pastoral Counselors might be hailed with less ambivalence if it were clearly addressing itself to the problems of identity, training, and the inter-professional place of the pastoral counselor and the mushrooming pastoral counseling centers or clinics. We can but hope that its formation does not further muddy the waters and that some day its or a similar organization's certificate will not be an empty wall decoration that impresses no one.[6]

Since we are limiting ourselves to certain problems of pastoral counseling, there is another "stickler" that meets our eye. In his book,

[6] See Seward Hiltner's article, "The American Association of Pastoral Counselors: A Critique" in *Pastoral Psychology*, April, 1964.

written for a psychoanalytic audience, Dr. Karl Menninger addresses himself to the problem of the "neutrality and ethics of the therapist."[7] He states that "neutrality in the analyst is one of the essentials of psychoanalytic treatment, but neutrality does not mean wooden aloofness. It means, rather, a hovering attention to what the patient says, with the suspension of expressed moral judgment . . . No analyst should pretend that he takes no moral position in regard to what the patient may do. He will refrain from passing a moral judgment prematurely on what a patient mentions or fantasies or even contemplates doing . . . He will not announce a position of moral condemnation regarding what the patient has already done, but neither will he approve it or condone it."

Dr. Menninger thus acknowledges and points out the difficulty involved in the ethical system of the analyst. Although he makes it clear that the analyst may not *convey* his moral system to the patient, this does not mean the analyst is without one. It is safe to say that for the analyst the task and work of the analysis supervenes a moral indoctrination of the patient whether it comes about overtly or covertly. The well-trained psychotherapist or the analyst, by his own value-judgments, ranks psychological help or therapeutic outcome over other *particular* values that might be classed religious, ethical, or social. In the therapeutic situation the objective, which may not necessarily contradict either the patient's or therapist's value systems, is to further his patient's mental health. His own analysis or treatment may help him avoid thrusting himself in the way of the patient whether such interfering urges stem from his own neurosis, background, or ethical system. As difficult as this value-system problem may be for the analyst, he nevertheless lets his eye be "single." It is focused on therapeutic outcome. For the pastoral counselor who is not so lucky to be in an unequivocal role as psychological helper, it is double trouble.

Whatever might be his unperceived motivations for doing counseling (a psychological condition shared in various degree with all secular therapists), the minister has to come to some peaceful settle-

[7] *Theory of Psychoanalytic Technique* (New York: Basic Books, Inc., Publishers, 1958).

ment in regard to his own *conscious* values, particularly when they conflict with those of the parishioner. Does the pastor join the psychotherapist in the valued goal of treatment? Does he subsume this goal to "religious goals?" Or does he try to do both at the same time?

What seems to be one of the most popular approaches among counselors is to wear but one hat at a time. But bending over backwards not to be "judgmental" may be the unhappy, uncomfortable, defensive, and largely ineffectual stance of the counselor, not-now-minister.

Another troublesome aspect of this value-judgment problem is exemplified by the counselor with hidden evangelistic intents. His use of counseling is in the service of winning converts to his church; philosophy; or, at times, unwittingly, to the service of his own personal needs. For this kind of counselor, the counselee's needs or health gets subsumed to a "greater cause." It is an unusual pastor whose theological and practical approaches permit him any satisfaction in effecting a therapeutic result that may be mentally healthy by psychological standards (a result by which self-bondage is loosened, or emotional growth stimulated) but which results in apparent "anti-religious" consequences, e.g. divorce, decreased church attendance, change of churches, etc. A result that by psychological standards of mental health may be successful, may appear to be by religious standards of a particular pastor, a failure. The exact opposite may also apply. I recall a pastor attending our Alaskan seminars who felt he had "failed miserably" with his parishioner because he complied with her wish that she attend another church and counsel with a different minister. In spite of the fact that in this new setting "she has taken hold and is now doing very well" he felt that *he* had failed her. All he had "failed" to do was allow her to go without inducing great guilt on her part and presented her with the opportunity for help he could not offer.

This particular problem of conflict of values is the kind of problem that *demands* a supervisory opportunity for the individual minister. No text on counseling or theology will bring an adequate answer because each minister must work out his own personal approach. But to have an uninvolved, supervisorily skilled second party with whom to discuss theological issues and their pertinence to counseling a particular case and to participate with such a person in counselee assessments is no luxury to a conscientious pastoral counselor. These kinds of efforts can only enlarge his armamentarium of help both religiously and psychologically. Who without the details of a case, for example, can say with certainty that a teen-ager who refuses to attend the church of his father and pastor, whose counsel he seeks, is not growing emotionally and spiritually? Such a refusal might be seen as a positive sign of the independent strivings of the boy struggling to become a man as easily as a negative indication of an arrogant rebellion against God.

It is a frequent interpretation of Jesus' beautiful parable that the returned prodigal son was healthier spiritually than the older son who served his father so faithfully (and bitterly). Momentarily if we could insert with tongue-in-cheek a hypothetical "counselor" who participated in helping the prodigal "come to his senses" this fantasied counselor might well profit from a supervised scrutiny of the details to evaluate his results in both spiritual and psychological spheres. The "supervisor" might ask, "Was the redemption of the prodigal consequent to his decision to return? To his hunger? To his leaving? Why did he leave and the older brother stay? Why was he urged to go back? What has happened after the homecoming party?"

Another bedeviling issue in pastoral counseling that is somewhat paradoxical is the *listening problem*. One of the remarkable achievements in the early development of pastoral counseling has been the establishment in the minds of pastors who counsel that they must listen. The point is a good one and it has been made. Within my experience in working with pastors the point has come back to haunt the pastoral counselor. Heard not infrequently from pastors in supervision is a kind of broken record, "I must listen, listen, listen." Although it is true that one must listen to arrive at diagnostic conclusions concerning a problem, the assumption that listening is always helpful is fallacious. Parishioners' words beating on the eardrums of a pastor may give him vibrations, but to expect their reception to be helpful in all, or even most cases, is an exaggeration of a good thing. The capacity to listen must stand in juxtaposition to the capacity to understand, the capacity not to listen, and the capacity to act. Listening rarely fails to be of service in diagnostic assessments, but therapeutically its uses are not universal and must be guided by diagnostic thinking and goals.

For example, if the pastoral diagnostic conclusion is that a parishioner needs to get something "off his chest" listening is a prerequisite for successful catharsis. But where other goals are important, listening as a therapeutic technique may do harm! I have found, for instance, that inexperienced caseworkers may listen avidly for weeks in order to "build a relationship" with their client. Not infrequently, and particularly if they have not done their diagnostic homework, they find the client in a deep dependent transference rut with them. While the student is "building a realtionship" by passive-receptive "understanding," the client has developed an intensely powerful attachment of a childlike nature wherein neither he nor the therapist are able to move. The "relationship" resembles that of Peter Rabbit and the Tar Baby. Attempts at disentanglement in such situations resembles the painful rupture of the separation that Peter Rabbit experienced. All in the interest of helping, therapist Peter Rabbit finds himself eventually covered with the tar of guilt, disillusionment and, sometimes, panic. The Tar Baby, could it experience as a client does, feels desertion, anger, and torn apart. More than once in my supervision of a case presentation the explanation for such a "relationship" is, "All I did was listen." Like any other therapeutic decision, the counselor must decide early *why* he is listening. If he wants to "build a relationship" he must also ask himself the all-important question, "In order to do what?"

For the most part I find ministers interested in counseling highly responsible and responsive to supervision. The minister "at the front" without help, without adequate training, and with courage in spite of uncertainty, has faired remarkably well overall. This is not simply a testimony to the inherent strengths of human beings who turn to the clergyman for help, but to the traits of pastors that convince us they are extraordinarily important forces in any one community's mental health problems. Those who do "wild therapy," fortunately, we find to be the exception. Percentage-wise they seem to be no more prevalent than those of other helping professions. The problems we have here discussed in the framework of pastoral counseling point toward the inevitable, namely, the institution of a kind of supervision that at the very least will help the pastor understand the psychological issues at stake in the counseling situation. Further, such a supervision will provide him with the armamentarium that will allow him to establish his appropriate and recognized place in the helping professions.

A fellow author in this series has answered the question, "How far should a minister go in counseling a parishioner?" with "as far as his training will take him." The principle here is sound. But the word "training" is the hooker. The pastoral counseling *specialist* must now measure his training by the inter-professional standards of the psychotherapeutic disciplines. Expedient measures and theoretical exposure with hints of supervision are introductory. Good training in psychotherapy rests on assimilation of a comprehensive, usable, theoretical system, guided clinical experience, and individual supervision administered by psychotherapeutic experts.

The pastor in the general practice of the ministry must be guided by his own past experiences, his common sense, and whatever local psychological resources there are available to offer him help, guidance, and direction towards making his contribution to his parishioners' and the community's mental health. Encouragement offered to medical students to follow certain obviously oversimplified principles of treatment may be useful to the pastor. "Do no harm. If what you are doing helps, keep it up. If what you are doing doesn't help, stop it. If you don't know what you are doing, don't do anything.".

The Problems of Referral and Consultation

Since it is an action based on a decision preceded by assessment, referral qualifies as an important aspect of pastoral treatment. Referral has been a prickly problem independent of the professional status of either the referral source or the receiving agent of help. But nowhere has it been more thorny or complicated than it is between psychiatrists and pastors.

It may be profitable to begin with the hindsight study of those people who have experienced referral. To help us with our perspectives of subjects' reactions to referral, we turn to findings of our own out-patient clinic at the University of Chicago.

> Advice to seek psychological help is usually interpreted by the patient in terms of his feeling about the person who makes the referral, his feelings about himself, and his bewilderment about the nature of his illness.

> Even when the patient has had a vague idea that he might need psychological help, he may interpret the suggestion as criticism, contempt, or rejection. Consequently, he may resent the person who made the suggestion. The most knowledgeable and sophisticated (patients) are not immune from such feelings, and many who do not yet recognize that psychological help can be of any real use to them interpret this suggestion as tantamount to being told there is nothing that can really be done for them. For any patient, referral to the psychiatric clinic is experienced to some degree as an abrupt separation from an important source of personal help, even when his referral is a sign of sincere and continuing interest. Unfortunately, the feelings of resentment are lost or too frequently not even acknowledged, and their expression is much less often encouraged by the referring person. We often suspect that referral to psychiatry has been made when communication between the patient and his referrant (referring person), has broken down. If the patient is still struggling to manage his feelings about the person who referred him, he is not very likely to relate effectively to the person who is now trying to help him.

> The patients often interpret referral for psychological help to mean that they are either "crazy, inadequate, weak or lacking in will power." The mutual understanding of the *individual* meaning and importance of these interpretations cannot be overemphasized. Being "crazy" sometimes is equated with a loss of control, often of sexual and/or aggressive impulses. Other patients appear to conceive of being "crazy" as being completely helpless and at the mercy of other people. Still others are primarily concerned that no one will take care of them or their children or of others who have been dependent upon them. Furthermore, referral for psychological help is almost invariably associated with a loss of self-esteem.[8]

The authors properly placed these excerpts in a setting of a section entitled, "Preparation of the Patient" for psychotherapy because

---

[8] Ralph Heine, Editor, *Student Physician as Psychotherapist* (Chicago: University of Chicago Press, 1962), p. 42.

referral is basically a *preparation process*. It is not an isolated act. Our experience is that those patients referred for psychiatric help who are "sent" or perhaps "dumped" without preparation, do poorly unless compensating factors, e.g. a motivation that overrides the destructiveness of the poorest referral, prevail.

Persisting momentarily in hindsight, what factors result in unsuccessful referral by the pastor? Three problems preventing adequate preparation are immediately outstanding: 1) the minister's failure to use his diagnostic skills to reach a firm conclusion, 2) disturbances in the pastor-parishioner relationship, and 3) an absence of or a breakdown in the pastor-psychiatrist (or other therapy agent) relationship.

1) The principles of pastoral diagnosis elucidated earlier are necessary antecedents to a minister's decision for the pastoral treatment which, in this case, is referral. If, however, his own brand of help rivals or supersedes other means of help, psychological help will be considered only under emergent conditions. The minister's apprehensions that keep him from useful diagnostic conclusions may encompass the following fears: a) fear that psychiatric help will be destructive or may result in deleterious "spiritual repercussions"; b) fear of the loss of his relationship with his parishioner; c) fear of the therapist or his methods secondary to inadequate acquaintance; d) fear of the parishioner's criticism; e) fear of shame, consequent to a "failure to help"; f) fear of guilt secondary to "causing" a parishioner's difficulty by inappropriate pastoral help that would be exposed in referral to another. These fears, among others, may create a partial paralysis that prevents decisive action. Since parishioners seldom fail to detect ambivalence, a referral without the pastor's full confidence may interfere with the parishioner's move toward appropriate help, especially when the pastor-parishioner relationship has been a powerful one. The stronger the importance of the pastor to his sheep, the greater will be the latter's sensitivity to the pastor's fear or uncertainty.

Adequate preparation for the final step in the referral process should include communication of those things that his parishioner can expect in the road ahead. Whether intentionally, or unintentionally, the pastor may mislead his parishioner into magical expectations, for instance, which, when unfulfilled in a first interview, may bring an abortive end to treatment. A rare but potent skill of preparation is the pastor's elucidation of *a* problem (if not *the* problem) which his parishioner can see and share with him which will offer a satisfactory handle on the psychiatrist's door. Early consideration of referral for those persons who present problems beyond his skills is another consequence of pastoral diagnostic acumen.

2) Disturbances in the pastor-parishioner relationship may precipitate an untimely dismissal. Referral may be simply an "accepting" way to reject the parishioner consequent to inadequate diagnostic judgment, development of threatening material and communications, a parishioner's provocations or serious counter-transference problems unseen by the pastor. (See discussion on "transference" p. 62. "Counter-transference" is the identical phenomenon with transposition of objects, that is, the *pastor's* illogical responses to his parishioner that have roots in his own personal history.) "I can't help you. Maybe a psychiatrist can." This may mean, "I don't like you or what you do— you deserve the punishment of dismissal to a doctor for crazy people."

A common phenomenon for all those who refer someone in whom there has been an investment is the referrant's protective concern. In exaggerated form, the concern may be symptomatic of an over-identification with the subject wherein the referrant vicariously experiences similar fears of anticipated treatment as the person referred. This over-protection may likewise preempt a useful preparation and visualization of problems. There would appear to be an optimal degree of concern by the pastor that allows him to be *with* the parishioner, yet permits him to "let go" in the same way he might accompany a patient to surgery confidently, but not with the expectation that he will "scrub-in."

3) If no relationship exists between sources of referral and helping agents, successful transfers rarely occur. Most "yellow-page" referrals are doomed. When the referrant is in darkness in his knowledge of the therapy agent, he has no greater titer of confidence than the level that would permit him to send his own child for surgery to an unknown. If, for example, the pastor has adequately prepared his parishioner for referral to a dynamic psychiatrist for psychotherapy, his efforts would be wholly wasted if the final choice of psychiatrists is one whose therapeutic armamentarium is limited strictly to the organic therapies. The patient is still unprepared.

If no relationship, knowledge, cooperation, or confidence exists between the minister and the psychological source of help, the pastor can hardly be of value in consummation of a referral. He may even be tempted inappropriately to welcome back to "safety" a parishioner who after one or two interviews returns with comments like, "I appreciate you, pastor. You understand me better than *he* does."

Breakdowns of communication between pastor and psychiatrist may be of a more subtle variety rather than the gross problems of an absent or openly oppositional relationship. Competitive interest, mutual fears, and distrust may all take their toll with the parishioner paying the price. Teamwork of unusual quality is required, especially with psychiatric patients.[9]

If we have focused our attention largely on the clergyman's role in referral, it is not only because this book is directed largely to him but also because ministers can hardly be expected to know the ins-and-outs of referral. A psychiatrist can claim no such innocence and, without going into details, he has developed a notoriously poor reputation for inter-professional relations, especially in "feedback." There are good reasons, as well as inexcusable ones for this unhappy state and often the former serve as rationalizations for the latter. The minister need not consider himself singled out by the psychiatrist to be ignored —physicians share this exclusion and are usually pleasantly surprised when a psychiatrist or psychiatric agent shares responsibility and information appropriately.

Turning to positive principles of referral, we can think of the latter as a preparation process similar to the task of a good mother who faces the first day of school with her 5-year-old child. She knows the day has arrived; she has spent time learning his concerns and allaying his fears appropriately; she knows the school, its reputation, and its quality of teachers and entrusts them with his care; she is not willing to sacrifice his growth potential by hanging on, over-protecting, or latently communicating her wish that he would not go (a common factor in school phobias). She confidently turns him over to the

[9] For the powerful effects of intra-staff difficulties on patients, see Alfred H. Stanton and Morris S. Schwartz's *The Mental Hospital* (New York: Basic Books, Inc., Publishers, 1954).

teacher for his own best interests, is ready to welcome him back after school, and is content with periodic reports of his progress. She will know that whatever skinned knees or emotional hurts he complains of will be, in part, some of his own making or perhaps distortion in his perception because she knows him, knows the school and the teacher's generally reliable reputation. If the mother-child relationship is healthy there will be no deception in the preparation process, no rewards for going, no tears at the door, no sitting in class and no blaming of the teacher for problems of the child. She would not consider sending him to a bad school, moving if necessary to meet his needs.

The three factors in referral just mentioned in a negative framework, can be transposed positively as well. 1) The diagnostic assessment of the pastor must reflect sufficient skill to recognize that a parishioner is long overdue for help; is an emergency; or needs assistance towards getting help in the future. There are situations where the optimal preparation process must be put aside. At times, whether the parishioner likes it or not (a very uncomfortable pastoral stimulus), he and his family may have to be guided to proper sources of care. Occasionally the sickest of patients protests vigorously that it is the world that is ill, not he. Often the protest is loud but superficial and he is greatly relieved when hospitalized. It is then a kindness, not a destructive or harmful action, to get such patients to havens for help, protecting them against suicidal, homicidal, or destructive intent and against the panic of psychological dissolution. It goes, without saying, that relatives must always be involved in the problem of hospitalization. They need help themselves in dealing with the impact of psychiatric treatment. They rarely fail, also, to be valuable sources of information to clarify the diagnostic picture.

Besides those obvious situations wherein immediate steps must be taken, there are less acute ones presented by the chronically mentally ill who, though not hospitalized, are largely paralyzed by their afflictions. Many of these ambulatory, "borderline" (on the margin of psychosis) patients seek out institutions from church to a general hospital for refuge. Institutions serve them as stabilizing Gibraltars outside unstable psyches. Many of these patients have been over the road of psychiatric help and, not infrequently, react to referral as a rejection. If they have never been treated or evaluated, they must be helped toward such a process that may offer much for stabilization. If they have been frequenters of psychiatric hospitals, consultation by a psychiatrist may be useful, not only directly to the patient, but indirectly to the clergyman who may either be unnecessarily anxious or appropriately perturbed in his role. Use of a working alliance with "half-way-houses" and organizations such as Recovery, Inc. may directly benefit the chronic patient.

It is not unusual for non-psychotic patients, who have severe psychological problems manifested by addiction to alcohol or drugs, homosexuality, prostitution, adult or juvenile delinquency, and promiscuity, to seek out a minister's help. The potential patient may not expect the minister to cure him but does hope for guidance to sources of help unknown to him or that he finds difficult to approach. Liaison with local groups, such as Alcoholics Anonymous or anti-delinquency organizations or mental health centers, may relieve a great load from the minister's shoulders. Unless pastors have had specific training of inter-professional quality for these problems, they leave themselves open to problems of foggy legal and medical responsibility; but more importantly, they may be likely to suffer the loss of great expenditures of energy if they undertake the *management* of these serious character-social problems.

In our experience it has been only the most psychologically sophisticated clergymen who recognize early the necessity of referral for the parishioner who has a specific neurotic symptom or character problems that do not disturb others flagrantly, or a constellation of difficulties for whom highly skilled psychotherapeutic help is the treatment of choice. Ministers have been inclined to think of psychotic patients as the charges of the psychiatrist and neurotic parishioners as candidates for pastoral counseling. Such a position of expediency is sound neither diagnostically nor therapeutically. Competent diagnostic skill in the assessment of neurosis is rare among pastors so that a general rule (always suspect) might be applied: all parishioners considered for a course of counseling without a psychiatric evaluation should present circumscribed, well-understood problems that have been met with successful management before in a reasonable time by a particular pastor's experience. Neurosis is not a mild psychosis; it is no less complex than schizophrenia. It requires the finest of treatment skills. It may be a potent recognized source of suffering and discontent but, when unrecognized, may be even more destructive to the person, his family, his church, and society than the flagrantly psychotic individual whose "craziness" keeps him free of crucial responsibilities. Government, business, armed services, and the Church itself have been aware of such destructive possibilities in ill-chosen workers. Increased attention and sophistication continues to develop in psychiatric screening for those in highly responsible stations, but the referring service of the minister "at the front" for his congregation and community is still a frontier.

2) As disturbances in pastor-parishioner relationships may prompt poor referral, constructive relationships may serve as a sound bridge to efficacious help. It is no accident that over 40 percent of emotionally disturbed people seek out the pastor first. The clergy has centuries of past tradition behind it as a friend of the sick and poor in spirit; and in its liberal tradition it adapts itself to meet present needs of people. It is so viewed by the public. The bridge to help provided by the pastor to his parishioner is like the bridge to health provided by mothers to their newborn. For months after birth the mother's antibodies against numerous diseases give the infant a running start until its own protective mechanisms are developed. A sound relationship between pastor and parishioner serves a similar protection and facilitates the development of trust in the treatment process. I find that most pastors and inexperienced psychotherapists grossly underestimate their impact on their parishioners or counselees. To appreciate the power of a parishioner's transference to the pastor, one needs to be on the receiving end of referrals a number of times to see the potent influence on feelings and behavior effected. The pastor catches an inkling of the strength of pastor-parishioner relationships when he comes to St. John's "to take *the reverend's* place."

3) Although community mental health should be primarily the concern of the psychiatrist rather than the clergyman, this is not always the case. The facts are that there are psychiatrists who care

little about community problems of mental health and care less about the pastor's role in spite of the figures that show the latter to be a crucial figure. Clergymen have wooed the psychiatrist, often unsuccessfully, to involve him appropriately in community needs. Preventive psychiatry has been, until recently, a still small voice. It is my conviction that the tide is changing and the need for wooing the psychiatrist's interests in the community and in the pastor will be increasingly reduced.

If President Kennedy's message to the Congress which specifically stipulated a priority concern for increasing programs in the treatment of mental illness and retardation is any indicator, the next 10 years will see vast changes in personnel and facilities.[10] There will be establishment of small local centers for diagnosis and treatment with the gradual abandonment of the large mental hospital, geographically distant from the patient's home. Management of patients is likely to be increasingly a movement from back ward to front ward, and from front ward to the front porch of the patient's home. The local influx of patients and personnel, together with awakening leadership in community mental health offered by men like Dr. Gerald Caplan, will demand community participation and incur professional cooperation now so little in evidence. The results of President Kennedy's program or ones similar are likely to be: 1) the pastor and his church, like the community and the nation, will have to get used to the presence of the emotionally ill, not their absence; 2) the increase in available professionals at the local community level that are interested in treatment and rehabilitation will force pastor and professional alike to deal face-to-face with heretofore "unnecessary" engagement in the care of patient-parishioner; 3) the pastor will be less likely to "lose" even temporarily, his parishioner to distant hospitals. If he could leave serious mental problems to the distant hospital and psychiatrist before, it will not be possible in the future. Likewise, the hospital psychiatrist will be looking for stabilizing resources on the home scene of his patients, whether these resources be family, agencies, rehabilitation centers or the Church; 4) for patients who formerly would have been hospitalized, other institutions like the Church in their solidity and

[10] House of Representatives Document No. 58.

stability will be singled out by them for comfort, support, and control; 5) although we can expect no defervescence of interest in the pastor's investment in counseling, we anticipate a much greater development proportionately in his capacity to bring psychological insights and principles into the garden-variety of his clerical responsibilities from teaching to preaching. This is not likely to come about because the pastor wants to serve the cause of mental health primarily, but rather from a vigorous dedication to serving the cause of man and his religious need.

I have been asked to address myself to a question mildly troublesome to pastors who counsel occasionally but vexing to those men who specialize as pastoral counselors. "Why is referral a one-way street between us and psychiatrists?"

Before examining the reasons why most referrals take the pastor-to-psychiatrist direction, it may be important to clear the air by stating my own biases first. As indicated in the first part of this book there are all kinds of psychiatrists, training orientations, and practices. Because a man has his M.D., three to five years of residency training or research, and even his specialty boards does not *automatically* mean he is a good or even competent *psychotherapist!* He may nevertheless be a capable psychiatrist, researcher, teacher, diagnostician, and physician; but these qualifications are not necessarily those of a psychotherapist. There are psychiatrists who are psychotherapeutic nihilists, do no psychotherapy and have no interest nor confidence in it. Nevertheless, they have had the training, experience, and credentials in baseline standards that qualify them appropriately as medical experts in psychiatric diagnosis and management. Their training entitles them to devote themselves to whatever methods of treatment they choose. Because some caseworkers, psychologists, and pastors are skilled and trained in psychotherapy they qualify to use its techniques, traditionally under medical auspices. In most states they are not considered "medical experts" as are all board certified or board qualified psychiatrists, whether the latter are trained in dynamically- or organically-oriented residencies. This standard legal position applies even though certain of these "non-medical" professionals *may* be more skilled as psychotherapists. Without getting overinvolved in this current confusion and states' legal variations, it is generally clear —and, I believe, appropriate—that the qualified psychiatrist is the number one medical-legal expert responsible in problems of mental health and illness. But skilled psychotherapists are still where you find them. I would like to think that skilled psychotherapists are in the majority in psychiatric ranks because of the established training opportunities available to them alone. The focal centers for the most thorough going and intensive training in a particular form of psychotherapeutic discipline are in psychoanalytic institutes which offer 5- to 10-year programs for psychiatrists and appropriate programs for other professional disciplines. Although one can find accredited psychoanalysts who do not measure up as psychotherapeutic experts, it is not because they have not been exposed to the very best possible training now available in any psychotherapeutic discipline.

These observations, biases, and convictions reflect my high regard for qualified skilled psychotherapy, regardless of the profession; my esteem for the basic training of all psychiatrists and the specialized training of psychoanalysts; and my respect for the medical-legal-moral responsibility for patients.

Out of many reasons for the one-way street in referrals, the following have occurred to me:

(1) Though there is a great range in the quality of psychiatric residencies, the basic standards are high and all the better ones require competence in psychotherapeutic experience and supervision. Incompetent or untrainable residents are not selected by good residency programs, or if selected are soon "washed out." Reliable qualifications, however, for a pastoral counselor to do psychotherapy (as we earlier defined it) are still nebulous. Even at their best they do not pretend to approach the psychotherapeutic training available to physicians in psychiatric residencies or in psychoanalytic training. Although pastoral psychology's growth has mushroomed since World War II, psychiatry's has exploded during the same period. This discipline, for the first time in medical history, takes its place at the side of other medical specialties in the clinical curricula of good medical schools.

(2) In spite of the rapidly growing training programs for pastoral

counselors, most psychiatrists and personnel in the mental health field do not know of these developments which are still sufficiently non-traditional to the uninformed for them to question their reliability.

(3) If a competent psychiatrist, trained and experienced in psycho-therapy, has a patient whose pastor views his trouble as a religious problem, the psychiatrist may, with good grounds, see it otherwise. Further, as noted in the first section of this book, there are many psychiatrists who still believe that any form of religious expression is either neurotic, psychotic, or in some way symptomatic and, therefore, belongs in *their* treatment territory. In my view an equally un-enlightened position is the one taken by those psychiatrists who believe that religion in any form is out of their territory and to be left alone as "too personal." Unprofitable and inappropriate referrals to pastors are made by these psychiatrists who pigeonhole religion or mistake a psychological problem for a religious one because it is wearing the trappings or guise of religious language. But even the most enlightened and sophisticated psychiatrists in matters religious have not yet seen clear indications for referral of their patients to pastoral counselors even when the problems of time, money, and competence are not issues. For example, many pastors have established a deserved reputation as marital counselors, but to the psychiatrist a problem described by a couple as "marital" may in his judgment have nothing to do with the marriage. In fact, it is quite unusual for a couple to come to a psychiatrist with difficulties whose *roots* lie in problems of marital adjustment. Communication breakdown, over-whelming external traumatic events, in-laws, problem children, birth control, monetary management, and sexual problems to name a few, may be the *stated* problems, but these *may* be an acceptable complaint of one or both members behind which stand glaring neurotic, psy-chotic, or character problems not amenable to ordinary techniques of marital counseling.

(4) Leadership for the cure of psyches decades ago moved from the Church to secular medicine. The revival of the Church's interest is relatively new. Psychiatry as a medical discipline benefits from medical tradition and appropriately assumes medical responsibility. Psychiatrists must be able to perform competently in the diagnosis,

treatment, and management of diseases of the mind, but must also show at least diagnostic sensitivity to diseases of the brain and body as well. For example, psychoanalysts are not just "souped-up" psychotherapists. Nowadays their postgraduate five years minimum of training in the art, skill, theory, and technique of psychoanalysis and their own psychoanalysis comes after their minimum of three years of special training in psychiatry which comes after their year of internship which comes after their four years of medical training. It is, then, not only a matter of psychotherapeutic training that contributes to the necessity for referrals to take largely the path from pastor to psychiatrist. Medical-legal-moral responsibility plays its appropriate role.

(5) As long as the distinguishing marks between different forms of psychotherapy are as vague as they are now whether each is labeled pastoral counseling, group work, casework, marital counseling, guidance, or psychotherapy, the standards of each will be gauged by the standards of the best. Although each of these forms has different characteristics and different services to offer, the specific credentials of the pastoral counselor are only gradually coming into definition. Unless his degrees or training include other established psychotherapeutic disciplines besides pastoral psychology, these very same disciplines, e.g. clinical psychology can only turn to the personal, not professional, qualifications of the pastoral counselor for assessment.

(6) Referral is not always an objective act determined by principles of good patient care. For example, in a corrupted medical practice the basis of referral may be as simple as a split fee. No more patient-oriented is the practice "you scratch my back and I'll scratch yours." Implicit, however, in even these shoddy referrals is a first-hand knowledge of the other's work. The pastoral counselor does not yet routinely travel in the known circles of mental health activity. Unless he is personally acquainted with sources of referral who know his work and trust him, he will not be thought of first.

(7) Another problem for the pastoral counselor is his motility. He could very well be the best qualified psychotherapist in his community, but if he moves every three to five years he cannot establish a reputation for good work in counseling. So crucial is a geographical

commitment that the physician can and literally does *sell* his practice because its establishment takes time, energy, and skill.

(8) Although a psychiatrist who is ill-equipped psychotherapeutically might refer a patient to a pastor for "counseling" by default, the psychodynamically oriented psychiatrist will but rarely encounter patients whom he expects to be specifically benefitted by the psychotherapy offered by a minister or a priest. It is far more likely that referral to the clergyman will be made because the psychiatrist sees the Church, pastor, and religion as offering some beneficial help that could not be effected by his own psychotherapy. (See "Religion as a Human Resource" Chapter Four.)

(9) Without going into details, reference in the early chapters to the problems that enter to plague the relationship between the psychiatrist and pastor may be enough to complete our review of those factors that make the road of referral not only rocky, but largely one-way.

Whether the pastor likes it or not, many psychiatrists do not yet picture the clergyman as a friendly established ally in the practical battle against mental illness. The tide is changing for several reasons. One of them is the pastor's interest in the problems of his community and his appropriate endeavors to improve it, his church, and his parishioners' state of health and mind. It has been a repeatedly pleasurable experience to have my psychiatric colleagues here and elsewhere who had never worked with clergy report with enthusiasm their surprise to find groups of priests, rabbis, and ministers not only busy at appropriate community problems but sharp in their understanding of psychology, eager to enlarge their views of human motivation, and curious to learn what the psychiatrist could offer them for their pastoral work's improvement.

The psychiatrist in private practice is not likely to look up a pastor, but this need not prevent the reverse if the pastor is eager to build toward a working relationship with him. Although this introduction might revolve around a parishioner, one of the most successful introductions to a functional relationship is the enlistment of the psychiatrist's teaching interests. Many psychiatrists are pleased to give their time to hold seminars. Since, however, it is their time and skill that brings their income, honoraria may be appropriate. A dual function may be served if a psychiatrist can be induced to supervise a minister or group of ministers. Such kinds of activities not only swell a minister's capacity to serve his people, but also help the psychiatrist to know the pastor and his assets as an ally in the overwhelming problems of mental health.

Probably secondary to my dual training, I have had unusual opportunity to encounter one particular question in referral considerations. "How crucial is it for the therapist to embrace the same religious affiliation as the patient?" My own conclusions based on personal and supervised clinical experiences and on the study described in "Religion as a Human Resource" are: (1) in general, the choice of psychiatrist rests (as it does with other medical specialties) far more soundly on qualifications, skill, aptitude, and sensitivity than on formal religious or philosophical orientation; (2) when pastor and parishioner are apprehensive over the fate of the latter's religion, he should not be referred to a psychiatrist who is avowedly antithetical to religion in all forms; (3) psychiatrists who view a patient's religion as a neurotic target and personal challenge with the same excisive urge as a surgeon does toward cancer are still struggling with their own religious or philosophical identity; (4) patients who create a fuss about the denomination of their potential therapist often have questionable motivation or unquestioned prejudice or they consider themselves highly special; (5) a patient genuinely frightened of someone who "is not one of us" should start treatment with the best trained available person who is of his religious bent and may thereby be a bridge to more expert help if indicated; (6) psychiatrists who make a point of their particular religious orientation for referrals are often on the periphery of the mainstream of competent therapists; (7) the competent psychiatrist without anti- or pro-religious axes to grind will treat his patient's unconflicted religious views with respect and his conflicted ones with confrontation.

One of the elementary snares in referral is misunderstanding that goes undiscussed and unclarified. When someone says to a physician,

"I am referring you a patient," this usually is interpreted to mean, "I am sending you a patient for your own evaluation and treatment." When one speaks of a "consultation," however, the pastor is obligated to make clear what he is requesting. We psychiatrists are sometimes prone to hear a request for *consultation* mistakenly as a request for taking over a case and management of a patient. A consultation may mean (1) a diagnostic evaluation of the patient without assumption of treatment responsibility; (2) a communication of opinion without a diagnostic examination of the patient himself; (3) supervision of counseling; or (4) teaching a clinical case conference. If things are not clear, they must be straightened out as soon as possible for benefit of all concerned.

Another aspect of referral wherein clarity is crucial is the local psychiatrist's definition of a "good" referral. What he means by "good" can be learned only from him. To some psychiatrists any referral that brings a patient with some semblance of a mental problem is a good referral. To psychiatrists eager to get symptomatic people back on their feet as quickly as possible through somatic therapies, a referral of a character problem may only mean re-referral. In large communities there are psychiatrists who practice sub-specialties (from psychoanalysis to hypnotherapy) and those who are general practitioners of psychiatry. Whoever the local psychiatrist may be, his "denomination" of diagnostic and treatment interests should be known, and bilateral exchanges over these interests offer another bridge toward mutual cooperation and responsibility.

Although the following statements have been implied in the section on diagnosis and more strongly inferred in these comments on referral, they deserve unambiguous assertion. The medical field of psychiatry has the responsibility, privileges, and recognition of leadership in the realm of psychotherapy. Psychiatry has already established a functional and mutually profitable alliance with social work and psychology, and is working hard toward such an alliance with law, nursing, and the teaching professions—but up to the present has largely ignored its responsibility to the clergy (and the growing field of pastoral care). Until an alliance is established in any large scale, however, churches, pastoral organizations, e.g. The American Association of Protestant Hospital Chaplains, individual priests, rabbis, and ministers will hasten the day of functional liaison by their appropriate persistent efforts to work with us, "reluctant dragons."

Pastors are at the front lines of the mental health battle, ready to offer and give first aid while we psychiatrists, psychiatric social workers, and clinical psychologists are largely behind the lines tending to established cases. We psychiatrists as a group have not yet fully recognized the potential value of collaborating with the biggest army in our society of preventive mental health allies, nor the dangers invited if we tell them to "go it alone, do it yourselves, we are too busy saving lives." This is an invocation to pastors to be patient with us and to work diligently with those psychiatrists who do see the values and the dangers and who claim their leadership, responsibility, and privileges as pivotal professionals for psychological, interpersonal therapies.

The intent of this effort is not to offer a cookbook of psychiatry for pastors. Pastoral diagnosis is not psychiatric diagnosis, nor is pastoral treatment psychiatric treatment. The principles for enlarging psychological understanding of parishioners in "pastoral diagnosis" hopefully will not only serve to increase the pastor's understanding exercised in his pastoral work, but will introduce him to some of the ideas of psychiatry's thinking as an appetizer for actual bilateral teamwork in the real world of a shared community.

An analyst friend of mine told me that one of the biggest stimuli toward interesting him in working with pastors was his acquaintance with the following episode: A pastor was called by a frantic, desperately depressed parishioner who asked him that he give her over the phone "the final forgiveness of God" before she took cyanide she had stolen from a laboratory. Efforts to change her mind or convince her to come see him failed, so he asked her a final favor—to make *him* a cup of coffee while he was en route to see her. Alerting a psychiatrist who advised getting her to a hospital, the pastor arrived, had his coffee, took the cyanide away, and escorted her to the emergency room. My friend's comment was, "Too bad most preachers aren't that sharp. Him I could work with. I bet he didn't realize the psychodynamic impact on that woman when he asked *her* to make *him* a cup of coffee—or did he?"

Fees

Private psychiatric fees, like all medical expenses, are high. To look at the extreme, the total cost to a person for a psychoanalysis with a skilled analyst, at $25.00 an hour, four or five hours a week for three to five years requires in the neighborhood of $15,000 to $30,000! Prolonged private psychiatric hospitalization may exceed these figures. I cite these financial extremes to emphasize the importance of assessment. No one can afford to leap into such a costly enterprise unless such a course of treatment is indicated through a careful psychiatric diagnostic evaluation. Therefore, it behooves the pastor and his parishioner to have benefit of the best psychiatric diagnostic services available *before* any serious course of treatment is considered. An excellent evaluation, performed by the finest of psychiatric specialists, can be had for $25.00 to $100, a relatively small figure considering the stakes, financial and otherwise, that can accrue. A consultation, as contrasted to a referral for treatment, leaves open many courses of action, including the possibility of appropriate continuation of work by the pastor and/or psychiatrist. The medical responsibility for decision and recommendation lies, of course, with the psychiatrist, but the interested pastor should not be left out. Indeed he might be expected to participate usefully in a plan of action, provided an inter-professional relationship is established. No pastor can afford to be burdened by the awesome threat of responsibility taken inappropriately, and no psychiatrist looks favorably upon counselors who make psychiatric diagnostic decisions. The price of the skilled psychiatrist's diagnostic hour becomes small indeed in its potential value for appropriate treatment planning and execution.

Ministers, who find themselves in a locale where there are no psychiatrists or none with psychotherapeutic qualifications may be tempted to treat parishioners themselves, abetted by what may serve as a rationalization, "there are no resources here." The time is fast arriving when qualified psychiatric resources are available every-where, at least for diagnostic purposes. Travel improvements have so condensed time and space that clergymen must think twice before abandoning the effort to get their parishioners to competent psychiatrists when diagnosis or consultation is indicated. This spatial condensation that brings excellent psychiatric consultation "next door" struck home when, in 1963, Dr. Carroll Wise and I were sent by the Western Interstate Commission for Higher Education to conduct mental health workshops in Alaska. The round trip covered 10,000 miles. The key psychiatric person in planning the seminars, Dr. J. Ray Langdon, practicing in Anchorage, reported that patients are sent to him from all parts of huge Alaska, and he himself "commutes" to Fairbanks to see patients, 400 miles away. One pastor flew in for the workshop from Pt. Barrow, hundreds of miles distant.

Certain principles that have pertinence to pastors might be worth mentioning about fees especially since currently large numbers of church-linked clinics or counseling centers have sprung up and many more are planned.

A fee, or its absence, is almost always an important aspect of treatment to the patient. It is invariably loaded with meaning, but its meaning is rarely the same to any one patient. As a therapist and supervisor of medical students, psychiatric residents and pastors, I have found that problems over fees are as much the problem of the therapist as they are the problem of the patient. Unless the therapist is free of discomfort in setting fees, it inevitably becomes a "patient issue." Even when no fee is charged, I have heard clichés like, "If you don't charge a mildly sacrificial fee or something (!) a patient won't think treatment is worth anything." This "explanation" may simply be a rationalization for the therapist's uncertainty in the matter.

The therapist whose income depends on the fee from his patients arrives at his own system of assessment. The system is rarely objective and may be established for various reasons, logical and illogical. The system may be based on the going rates of others of equal training, on his competence, on his conscience, on his chosen social class of clientele, on his value systems, on his view of himself, on patient income, on his wife's needs, on his own analyst's standards—and, oh yes, on his skill. As ambiguous and varied as the actual reasons may be for a system of fees for psychiatrists in private practice, the pastor or pastoral clinic struggles with an additional problem, i.e. the tradition of no fees for services of pastors, whether they be associated with conducting funerals, performing weddings, or offering counsel.

Unless the therapist is relatively unconflicted over the fee, he is not likely to arrive at an understanding of the patient's individual interpretation of the fee. The variety of responses is as kaleidoscopic as the meanings attached by patients to gifts they may wish to present to their therapists. Whereas willingness by one patient to pay a high fee may indicate strong motivation for help and change, to another it may be a means by which he may "buy off" the therapist, use it defensively against change and as a subterfuge for absent motivation. A low fee may for one patient be truly sacrificial while to another, although equally sacrificial, its token value may be scoffed at and serve as an external trapping for derision of the therapist. To illustrate additional varieties of the near infinite responses to fees of patients we cite: (1) the depressed patient who states the fee is too high and that he cannot afford treatment because he feels he is not worth spending anything on and does not deserve help anyway; (2) the dependent patient who allows his bills to spiral because institutions and collectors, at least, become interested in his welfare and their badgering serves as reassuring contact; (3) the paranoid patient who wonders if he is not being treated uniquely as either someone special or someone plotted against; (4) the penurious obsessive to whom any fee is sacrificial; (5) the obsequious passive patient who pays anything, immediately, to avoid open conflict; (6) the striving competitive woman for whom the bill, regardless of its appropriateness, is the signal to begin the fight; (7) the hysteric woman who erotizes the bill into a love note and carries it in her purse so "something personal" of the therapist will be close to her. The pastor must not be thrown off guard by patient's unrealistic responses to either psychiatrist fees or fees set by him and his church organization. If, however, he has his own axes to grind in this respect, be they reactions to or against his conscience, competitive strivings, or whatever personal problems enter into fee setting and collection, one important lane into the patient's problems is cut off—the avenue of the fee.

Because of a specific nature of fee arrangements we are forced to limit ourselves to the few principles mentioned. One final comment may serve those who work in a pastoral counseling center wherein operations are not dependent on fees of clients. Do not expect people routinely to respect the therapy less because they are not charged or vice versa! The "no charge" or "free-will offering" is as loaded a question in the client's treatment as any fixed fee that might be charged. Those clients who make an issue of the no charge fee (or one based on a sliding income scale) are offering, as the saying goes, "grist for the mill." My own conviction shared with colleagues is that no counseling center, whether church-affiliated or not, should be without the benefit of consultative service of the most gifted supervisory psychiatrist available. His knowledge can be tapped not only for fee planning but also for his counsel in those patient-staff reactions to the fees that are set in the counseling process.

CHAPTER FOUR

RELIGION as a HUMAN RESOURCE

Religions have a history as ancient as man himself. Whatever hoary civilizations that have been unearthed by archeologists or primitive cultures studied by anthropologists, these have all had, to my knowledge, some form of religion as primitive or as sophisticated as its adherents. A ready explanation for religion as a common denominator of man's world falls readily from theologians' lips: "Before man was God; from ancient days God has been revealing Himself. However strange have been the means of worship and belief, these are but the unfolding leaves of God's revelation and man's response to Him culminating in our (whatever religion one has chosen) final revelation." With each new age discoveries that unveil mysteries in the world of man have evoked theological crises with the skeptic ready to abandon gods or God and believers revising their theology and interpretations. The belief in a flat Earth or a Heaven overhead are examples of old convictions delegated to myth by enlightened religions.

No matter how traumatic discoveries have been to theological concepts, *religions survive!* Although we may assume that God is forever and unchanging, man's *concepts* about Him have changed and continue changing. Whether we accept the theologians' explanations for the persistence of living religions as man's eternal response to God or the atheists' charge that God is but a creation of man, for the purposes of this work the important issue is that *religion appears to be as integral a part of man's history as his consciousness.* So intimate with the nature of man is his religion that Judao-Christian tradition has associated it with breathing. The "pneuma" of God gave man birth and life.

Among many possible explanations for the survival of religions, a simple, perhaps naive, one appeals. Religion has survived because man has survived. For whatever reasons, he has preserved a religion for himself to meet his needs. Living religions serve man's needs; those sects and cults that are deceased died when man's needs were unfulfilled by their provisions.

Largely on the basis of a study to be described in brief, we have observed that psychological needs *are* met by religions which serve as human resources. Freud associated need with wishes and with psychological manifestations of the drives which he considered constitutional, ever present and demanding satisfaction. (See p. 66.) For our purposes we can say that a need is a persistent demand for gratification that is appreciated psychologically but rooted in man's constitution. Thus a living religion provides psychological means for meeting demands that are rooted in man's constitutional being. A dying or dead religion fails to provide these means and is cast aside or atrophies with disuse.

A clinical study made with colleagues Drs. George Meyer, Zane Parzen, and Gene Samuelson at the University of Chicago Hospitals and Clinics is highly influential in forming the basis of opinion for much of what is said here of religion as a human resource.[1] In brief, this detailed study of 50 patients in and out of the hospital established the psychological diagnostic value of patients' religious beliefs and activities. Identification of patients' psychological makeup, character structure, personality strengths and conflicts through the assessment of their religious practices and ideation alone, without knowledge of their clinical material, became possible. The study showed very clearly that religion serves many of the psychological needs of people. They invest in those aspects of their religion that are currently of psychological importance. Regardless of denomination or sect they interpret

[1] Scientific paper presented at the annual meeting of the American Psychiatric Association, May 1964, Los Angeles, California. A summary of "The Contribution of Patients' Religious Investments to Psychiatric Understanding" may be found in the Scientific Proceedings of the American Psychiatric Association 1964, page 167. An article entitled, "On the Diagnostic Value of Religious Ideation" was published in the *Archives of General Psychiatry*, September, 1965.

their formal religion's doctrines individually and personally. It was equally clear that religions do not serve sick aspects of the personality only. Nor is religion simply associated with superego or conscience functions of the mind but is as intimately expressive of primitive drives (id) and integrative operations (ego). Furthermore, and basic to this discussion, religion was found to be linked with the psychological developmental progress of the personality.

A full description of what might be termed "a developmental theory of religion" (the psychosexual developmental correlates of religious expression) must be deferred. Suffice it to say here that we have found that for each step of the psychosexual scale of personality development there are corresponding religious attitudes. For example, a highly narcissistic person will have his religion centered on himself —there to serve his own omnipotence. The delineation of ego strengths and weaknesses (see pp. 48f.) can be translated into corresponding varieties of religious expressions. Vastly oversimplified, infantile characters have infantile religious convictions while mature personalities find highly sophisticated means to express religious feelings or philosophical views.

In the study a religious history was obtained in a structured interview with additional questions designed to evoke religious ideas of each patient conducted by a person untrained psychiatrically. This data proved to be remarkably unveiling of the person himself, sufficient to allow an accurate psychiatric evaluation without clinical information.

Each of these cases was studied in great detail but space inhibits a detailed account here. However, a brief illustration of the revealing nature of religious ideation is indicated. The young woman cited earlier (page 67) who had a streetwalking phobia chose as her favorite Bible character, Mary Magdalene. She said, "Not many people know she was a prostitute." Looking externally for means to shore up her own weakened inner controls, she saw her religion as important to her because "it's black and white. You need other people to tell you what's right or wrong." She chose as her favorite Bible verse, "Blessed are the pure in heart for they shall see God."

None of the 50 patients in the study were considered to suffer from religiosity (an abnormal preoccupation with religion) but all had their own religious or philosophical ideas which offered the researchers plenty of useful material for assessment. Although the patients' religious ideas at times revealed their serious psychological conflict, they as often revealed reflections of their individual personality strengths, traits, and defenses.

In the past, institutionalized religion has never been particularly troubled over its bizarre adherents, wild movements, peculiar saints, lascivious Brahmans, paranoid preachers, disturbed rabbis, eccentric bishops, or psychopathic popes. Nor has it seen fit to acknowledge character strengths in those heretics, reformers, or rebels who opposed its teachings. In short, it had not been interested in the personality sources of religious manifestations but rather had stood ready to acclaim hysterical or psychotic phenomena as signals of the Holy Spirit. This view is changing radically and rapidly. But some religions continue to deceive themselves like the naive woman whose boy went to see the psychiatrist. She told her neighbor, "All this nervous fuss over a Greek myth? Oedipus smoedipus, just so he loves his mother!"

I once heard a famous evangelistic missionary introduce a young woman on a fund-raising tour with him as "the human being closest to Jesus I've ever encountered." This poor girl spoke of enduring her mother's burdening final illness by assuming she was caring for Jesus and rubbing his back like she had her dead husband's. She went on to tell of her intimate conversations with birds in the bushes that guided her (literally) to do righteous acts and told her (literally) how to love God and serve man. Like many in that startled congregation, I did not need any psychiatric training to know the girl was psychotic, more in dire need of help, than exhibition as a "maiden of Jesus." I suspect the cause of the missionary, so long esteemed, suffered more harm than good through his innocent but poor judgment. The point here is that religion has not gone about planning its beliefs, ritual, practices, and orders so that they are tailored to mental health or pathology. Rather, for better or for worse, in sickness and in health, it offers a unique means dedicated to meet man's psychological needs. Until recently, organized religions have not been interested in the question, "Are the religious beliefs and activities of this particular person psychologically healthy, defensive, homeostatic, or destructive?"

Religion as a human resource meets needs or it does not survive. A brief analysis of the varying forms religious manifestations may take to provide psychological aid, comfort, or stimulus is indicated. These manifestations have been alluded to in psychiatric, but especially psychoanalytic, literature. Freud, the father of modern psychiatry, has been the major contributor to the methods for the study of psychological phenomena in patients. But his willingness to generalize his understanding of religion removes a bit of the steam from his contribution in this particular area. For example, in his major work directed to religion, he standardizes all religions by one brand of Protestantism.[2] He accounts for God as man's projection of the human finite father.[3] His scientific zeal halts him, however, after various other generalizations, e.g. "Religion would be the universal obsessive neurosis" that arises out of the Oedipus complex. He reminds himself, "but these (statements) are only analogies, by the help of which we endeavor to understand a *social* phenomenon; the pathology of the *individual* does not supply us with a fully valid counterpart."[4] It is precisely to this point that our study of the individual's uses of religion for psychopathological, homeostatic, or healthy purposes serve us well in analyzing its psychic functions in *a* person, not people or society in general. As non-patients are not completely healthy, our patients were not sick through and through. We studied their healthy psychological mechanisms as well as their pathological ones and found religious phenomena expressing both.

Our study indicates a general readiness of the mind to use religion psychologically not only as reflections of struggles of the Oedipal stage of personality development but pre-Oedipal and post-Oedipal as well. That is, we found religion lending itself as a vehicle for the expression of psychological development up and down the psychosexual scale of personality growth. Further, we found no one aspect of the mind, whether the id, the ego, or the superego to be the

[2] *Future of an Illusion, op. cit.,* pp. 18–20.
[3] *Ibid.,* p. 17.
[4] *Ibid.,* p. 53, italics mine.

dominating psychological structure in religious ideas or meanings. We found that religion offered host to primitively expressed id wishes as easily as it provided reinforcement of ego defenses. For example, with our evangelist's companion, id wishes taking the form of erotization of the figure of Jesus whose back she believed herself to be rubbing stood right beside the ego mechanism of reaction-formation that kept her hostility against her mother hidden by her "love."

In brief, our study indicates that religion can be used in remarkable ways to meet various psychological needs and wishes. Most denominations are sufficiently grand in the scale of their ideation, practices and traditions that any one individual can find what *he* needs in his own church. But if that church does not so fulfull him he moves around until one is found that does. Though there may be one set of definitive doctrines in his particular church polity, our study shows clearly that he will interpret orthodoxy unorthodoxly, and will re-tailor it to suit his personal life style or current psychological state.

Psychological Manifestations Expressed in Religious Forms

Psychiatrists, unless grinding their own anti-religious axes, do not *blame* religion for their patients' delusions of grandeur which involve God, Jesus, or Mary any more than they hold Napoleon responsible for psychotic identifications with the little Corsican. (They might ban religious material that they consider destructively stimulating to patients whose psychoses are entangled with religious preoccupations in the same way they would keep Napoleonic tracts from patients possessed delusionally with Bonaparte. But that is a different story.) Further, they view delusions and hallucinations not as bad, but as symptoms of ego defects which are serving as last-ditch primitive defenses against complete psychological dissolution or against impulses or wishes too overwhelming to tolerate or acknowledge and that require that they be projected or thrust "outside" the self. Thus even psychotic manifestations can be viewed as useful in a peculiar way. A psychologically sick person's use of religion does not necessarily indict the religion as sick for others any more than the acceptance of a religion of merit exempts the devotee from illness. Psychiatrists fail to attribute the attainment of psychological health to the fact that a person has a belief in God. The borders between psychological health and neurotic or psychotic manifestations are often fuzzy. The delineations are only clarified by intensive study of the individual in question.

The following case vignettes serve as examples of the nearly infinite variety of forms that psychopathology may take in using religious trappings, symbols, ideation, customs, or traditions. All of these illustrations are drawn either from our study, from my own experience in treating patients, or in supervising medical students, pastors, and psychiatric residents.

CASE 1. *Religion used as a dropped hanky for a "successful evangelist."* A young, attractive woman was referred by her husband to our clinic "because she is too religious." The husband's real complaint was that his wife was interested in converting men to *her* and used religion like a dropped handkerchief as a means of beginning affairs. She herself had no complaints and began treatment with an attempt to convert (unsuccessfully as far as I know) a befuddled senior medical student with her "theology."

CASE 2. *Religious ideation used as a control for bothersome impulses.* Besides the woman cited earlier whose sexual wishes were out of control and whose favorite Bible character was Mary Magdalene, a patient of mine had specific difficulty with his aggressive impulses. This man, a pastor, was frightened by his wishes to hurt and developed a transient phobia of performing in the communion service. His specific fear was that as he performed his priestly duty, he might spill the wine which to him represented someone's blood, literally. As long as he consciously convinced himself that the whole thing was "symbolic anyhow and nobody was really hurt, except a long time ago," he felt at ease.

CASE 3. *Religion used as a whip by a smothering mother.* A young teen-age girl came to see me with a fear of going to school. She was unconsciously afraid to leave her mother, "who might die when I'm away." The mother was a strict adherent of a fundamentalist sect. She continually sought to get her daughter "saved." But the patient's growing pains of adolescence prompted her to start wearing lipstick, going to movies, and acknowledging that she was, unlike her mother, unsaved. The patient dreamed one night that her mother died. This so frightened her that she awoke on her knees praying for God's forgiveness. The next weekend at church she was "saved" and was "reconciled" to a hostile dependent relationship with her mother. She abandoned her normal adolescent attempts to emancipate herself at least for the time being.

CASE 4. *Religion used as an army against the enemy within.* A lost, isolated young Negro man continually at odds with himself had un-recognized deep-going resentment against his brother and mother, whom he described as "socially-minded religious liberals." The patient was introduced to the Black Muslim group and became a fanatic. He was suddenly prejudiced against all Whites and any "so-called Negroes" who did not belong to Elijah Muhammad's flock. Especially did he despise members of the NAACP. The war between his rageful wishes toward his family and his criticizing conscience moved from inside himself to the outer world. The Black Muslim doctrines became ego-syntonic (unconflicted) for him. His conversion meant to him, "For the first time I found peace" (!)

Other uses, among many, made of religion as a psychological smor-gasbord, include religion used as a cleaning solution for dirty thoughts, as an antidote for poisonous fears, as a retreat from world temptations or human closeness, as a mother-substitute for orphaned feelings, and as a battleground for competitive strivings. This last usage may be of particular interest since my patient in this instance was a contentious minister's wife, a woman with strong masculine traits and competitive ambitions who came for help because "I have lost faith in God and you know what that could do to my husband's career!"

Religion's Resources for Equilibrium and Development

An interesting and extremely important development in the theo-retical and technical realms of psychoanalysis has taken place in the last 30 years. Whereas Freud and his colleagues' early discoveries and formulations focused on the working of the id, considered as the primitive reservoir of the drives in the structure of the mind, in the twenties the integrative adaptive functions of the ego took the foreground of Freud's interest. With the primary debt to his leadership, his followers, including his daughter Anna, and Heinz Hartmann, (the current leading theoretician of psychoanalytic thought) have brought us through the threshold of ego-psychology to the present interest in the whole of man's mind as the focus for scientific, theoretical, and therapeutic attention.[5] This shift of attention has removed psychoanalysis from its focus on "abcess" theories and psychopathology to its interest in character analysis, repair, synthesis, and adaptation. Modern psychoanalytic treatment is directed toward seeking alliances with the ego rather than exposing the id or clobbering the superego. This shift in theory and technique resembles analogically the internist's efforts to assist the host against the assault of disease more than the surgeon's excision of pathological tissue. "Where id was, let ego be," and "Make the unconscious processes conscious," carry no pejorative charge to modern "psychosynthesists."

This ego-oriented theoretical framework demands that we psychiatrists reexamine many of man's established institutions, including religion, not only in the searing beam of id-oriented psychopathology but in the synthetic rays of ego adaptation. Let me remind the reader that psychiatric interests in the psychological aspects of religion have until recently focused on its "pathological" services to sick psyches. Religious delusions, hallucinations, religiosity, and scrupulosity have become common topics in psychiatric literature; one could almost say, they have become worn out themes.[6] The skimpy treatment we offer here can only give flavor to understand what is yet to come in psychoanalytic investigations of religious functioning that are trained on the ego.[7]

[5] See *The Ego and the Mechanisms of Defense* by Anna Freud and *Ego Psychology and the Problem of Adaptation* by Heinz Hartmann (New York: International University Press, 1958). (Actually written in 1937.)

[6] A waft of refreshing air drifted into some of the discussion on religion at the 1963 psychoanalytic convention in St. Louis. See *Journal of the American Psychoanalytic Association*, Vol. 12, January, 1964, "Clinical and Theoretical Aspects of Religious Belief," p. 160.

[7] See Marjorie Brierley's *Trends in Psychoanalysis* (London: Hogarth Press, Ltd., 1951), pp. 246–290.

Most psychotherapists would agree that for treatment to be effective, the patient must experience a vaguely delineated optimum titer of anxiety. He has to be sufficiently bothered and, therefore, motivated to change. An overwhelming charge of anxiety reduces immediate workability and demands relief, while no anxiety makes treatment unworkable. Likewise, most of us attempt to help patients avoid psychosis or neurosis (except under very special conditions wherein these torments might be necessary antecedents to treatment goals, e.g. in the development of a transference neurosis). For psychological growth and development, most child psychiatrists feel that optimal frustration with a backdrop of confident trust is a requisite stimulus for positive growth changes; whereas, overwhelming anxiety will inhibit or regress the child, and absent frustration without anxiety will tend to fixate the growth process. Perhaps the positive psychological values offered by religion can be similarly classified as it aims to reduce overwhelming charges of psychological stress and yet offer stimuli to needle the apathetic—"to comfort the afflicted and to afflict the comfortable."

A major kind of psychological contribution which religion may offer is its resources to ameliorate overwhelming anxiety. To the weak ego, stress that might be adjudged as minor for most people, may bring overwhelming anxiety. We note that religion, while it cannot alter the precipitating stress, may alter the degree of pathological response. It can and does perform a similar useful service to the strong ego when stresses of acknowledged magnitude assail. A hospital chaplain friend told me that soon after he arrived at his hospital he was sought out by surgeons because they felt the preoperative and postoperative courses of a number of panicky patients who faced operations were helped by his visits. I learned from a surgeon there that "he (the chaplain) has the ability to help the patient relax and let us do the driving." What this particular man seemed to be able to do in a remarkable way was to inspire confidence in his hospital parishioners. It is common knowledge that to some extent medical patients "must become as little children," welcome the authority of the physician and his medical regime, and "turn on" the trusting, submitting qualities that speed recovery. This ability to "regress in the service of the ego" may be augmented by religion whether the stress be an operation, sickness, death, or the business chaos encountered by a tycoon Atlas, holding the Earth on his shoulders. The omniscient, omnipotent protection of one's own God has been a comfort and reliance for men facing stress through the centuries. Whatever its sources, its psychological function and potency to the faithful is incontrovertible. (It is an open philosophical question beyond this book whether or not the faith and basic trust of the adult in one's God and fellow men lies rooted in his earliest relationship to his mother as an infant.)

A middle-aged, depressed woman sought treatment several months after her mother was killed in an automobile in which the patient was driving. She indicated that the only thing that kept her going during the shock stage was her faith in God. "If it hadn't been for my religion, I would have lost my mind." She may have been right. The great bulwark of her religion in various modes had helped sustain her sanity. An interesting twist, however, in this particular case was that one particular aspect of her belief shielded her destructively and prevented the evolution of grief to proceed. Although she had loved her mother she had hated her, too. The only conscious hints of the extent of her hate were various moments in her lifetime when she had feared, irrationally, for her mother's death. She required continual reassurance from her pastor after the accident that "mother was in God's hands, safe and unharmed"—from her unrecognized wishes! As she worked through her ambivalent feelings toward her mother in treatment, she grasped why the one particular line of the Lord's Prayer had been so meaningful at the time of her mother's death. The line was, "Thy will be done," ("not mine").

Another one of the ways religion serves psychologically as a human resource is its permission to adherents with healthy egos to "regress" with approval. Whether "leaning on the everlasting arms" or looking "up unto the hills from whence cometh my help" or affirming "Thy rod and Thy staff they comfort me," the believer's ego, under stress, is allowed to lean, look for help, and be comforted. For those with unhealthy egos that must lean, look for help, and seek comfort as a life occupation, religion offers haven and satisfaction without the induction (necessarily) of guilt stemming from dependent, infantile yearnings.

For some people whose early lives were an inferno and the only kind of human warmth known was paid for with a painful, searing heat, religion and the Church offer a kind of safe middle-ground in which these people, so frightened of human closeness, can set their own pace in human communications. They may need the structure of the Church, including its models of the Holy Family, to keep in touch. These unfortunates seldom draw close to the human representatives of the Church's structure. They reach intermittently and very tentatively out for human warmth, fearful out of their past and early life that such warmth may burn them. The doctrines of a caring God manifested in this world by a concerned clergy or a community of believers may be just the right milieu for those with the right to be frightened of close human relationships.

The search of the adolescent for the ideal is a remarkably devoted one. Here again the Church's interest in youth offers very concrete psychological assistance. A young tough with a long police record, ostracized by schoolmates as a "hood" was referred for psychiatric evaluation to me after he had been caught stealing from his own church's box for the poor. His belligerent explanation was, "The poor will never see that dough with those dishonest, fat priests to get their crumby hands on it. What fakes they are. They're the modern money changers! The real followers of Christ are out helping the poor. If people really followed and believed in Him this'd be a good world to live in." As mixed up as this modern Robin Hood's views were, he longed for an ideal which he felt had been abandoned by religion's representatives. Because adolescence is so tumultuous and pubescence brings surges of drive demands, youths find the idealism of religion and philosophy appealing to give them purpose and worthfulness, to shield them from threatening impulses, to offer outlet from overstringent chastisements of the conscience, to present heros of merit as "replacement" for parents with feet of clay and to assuage the guilt of their sexual, often masturbatory, explorations.

Important bastions of defense against anxiety, the ego mechanisms, are served by religion's structure (see page 50). We can but illustrate one or two other mechanisms besides those mentioned in the several cases cited. Intellectualization is an ego mechanism which, in effect, robs or dilutes appreciation of feelings or affects by strangulation with ideas. It is one of several mechanisms (isolation, reaction formation, doing and undoing) whose constellation is seen in obsessive-compulsive personalities. A young theological student complained that he wasted time by compulsive rituals designed to keep his room orderly or else isolated himself by studying only theology. Theologies intrigued him to the point of preoccupation. He thought the book title "Man's Disorder and God's Design" described himself. His symptoms began when he got a "C" in a course of a particular professor whose "haughty pride got to me." He was fearful that his anger at the professor, "if known, would blow up the whole Divinity School." Although he had always been inclined to keep aloof through books, the tiff with the professor brought redoubled strength to the already present and necessary mechanisms of defense. Although his intellectualization became extreme and symptomatic, he had earlier found great relief in and useful dedication to the world of religious ideas.

One patient in our study who believed strongly in the "power of positive thinking" adapted to stresses by pollyanna responses which made use of the mechanisms of defense called denial, suppression, and reaction formation. Ego defenses expressed through religious ideation serve as regulatory mechanisms to preserve comfort and defend against stimuli that would arouse paralyzing anxiety. Their important preservatives need not only be respected, but at times reinforced. In the 50 patients we investigated, we saw repeatedly the manifestations of these mechanisms expressed through religious ideation.

The Church, like perhaps no other institution, can offer systems of belief and practices that structuralize solutions for unresolved and *unresolvable* childhood conflicts. In the shared conviction of the brotherhood of man, for instance, a person can find a universal solution for his individual private struggle with his real brother that has not found, and may never find, a peaceful solution. Another example of such a universal solution is the fellowship offered to individuals, each of whom may feel that *he* alone deserves to be called *chief* of sinners. The fellowship of shared responsibility for sinful thoughts or action serves as a tempering, diluting resource that alleviates the disabling guilt that one might experience if he actually were completely alone in his sins of despicable awfulness.

These illustrations of adaptive solutions offered by religion have largely been of the "status quo" variety, i.e. restitutive, homeostatic, or preserving of psychological comfort. They are not particularly stimulating to the growth of the ego. I feel that religions in their fullest potential can and do offer challenges and stimuli to psychological growth and are not simply trappings for universal neurosis or psychosis, nor simply ego supportive at their very best. Rather than an organizational compendium of such resources offered by religion, we are forced again by space to resort to illustration.

Psychiatric research of religion has focused on pathological mechanisms, and especially on the ways that religion expresses the harsh, restricting superego. There is no question but that some religious adherents offer fertile investigative grounds for pathological superego functioning, but that is not the whole story. Religion may play as important a role as well in offering expressions to a benign, self-approving superego and the ego ideal. Religion may as easily offer the stimulus to self-fulfilling and gratifying activities expressed in societal contribution as it can be a powerful inhibition to keep the animal urges and drives of the masses in check (Freud's major gratitude to religion's civilizing power).

Religion deserves as readily plaudits as an ally to creativity, a highly prized function of the ego, as it does as sorcerer of religious wars, persecutions, and ruthless actions of man's inhumanity to man. The "spark of the divine" and the spur of creativity in fine artists, great reformers, innovators, and inventive geniuses is just beginning to gain investigators' attention. It is of interest that from the beginning of Judao-Christian traditions God himself has been identified as Creator. Jesus, as author of "The truth shall set ye free," a basic tenet of any research, set a pagan world on its ear. His views and ideals continue to sponsor spiritual and social revolution.

Before turning to the specific resources of religion already organized to meet human needs, a last somewhat speculative function needs mention as an example of the kind of problem further psycho-dynamic research may approach in the future as psychiatrists' interests swing further from psychopathology to those phenomena that con-tribute to psychic health. An axiom of Freud's was that psychoana-lytic treatment aims to make the unconscious conscious. In his topo-graphical model of the mind the preconscious stood between the unconscious and the conscious mind. The energies of the repression barrier between the preconscious and the unconscious were lost to useful (love and work) ego functioning. His assumption was that energies were chained to unconscious conflicts. If these were brought to the surface, energies were divested from the conflict and made available for use to the ego. It seems to me altogether plausible that religious functions with their psychological impact may offer a vehicle for the transport of unconscious mental conflicts to the preconscious mind where their charge of bound energy becomes ac-cessible. For example, a patient of mine carried about a burden of paralyzing guilt of which he was but vaguely aware. Following a communion service occurring in the course of treatment, he felt suddenly "like a great weight had been lifted: I was a free man, off to a brand new start, no longer isolated from people but reconciled. Instead of feeling coldly towards people, I had a warm spot for them. Even my business competitor seems less of a villain. I feel like I've got energy to burn." The patient's account of what happened was that during the silent period before communion on a particular Sun-day, the minister as usual had called on the congregation to acknowl-edge both their inclinations to sin and their specific sins. At this time the patient became aware of his tremendous hate of his business rival and acknowledged his wishes for the latter's painful death. He accepted the idea that "Jesus had already died for this very sin of mine." The charge of guilt had rested deep in an unconscious con-flict, carried from childhood, that sprang from his repeated wishes for the eradication of his little brother. The latter, in the patient's mind, replaced him as his mother's favorite. This brother actually did die of leukemia when the patient was five. The patient, however, after this communion service was only aware that he felt exonerated from responsibility for his hateful thoughts to his living peer and that Jesus' death washed away his crime. The next day, as the first day of that work week, the patient had gone to his non-plussed competitor, confessed his past alienation and literally obtained the rival's forgiveness which "only added to my feeling of freedom and inner happiness." Although this guilt of his had been carried for years, and he had attended many previous communions, this particular service carried a lasting impact. It came during a time when he was working through active competitive feelings with me which he had thought dangerous. This episode was, therefore, probably related to the treatment process. However, I want to emphasize that he came for treatment because of his isolation from his wife, not specifically because of his trouble with his peer though these two problems were related in his history. (His Oedipal striving was to get brother and father out of the way to his mother's heart.) I do not mean to undercut the impact of his treatment but this breakthrough came in a service designed for the acknowledgment and the forgiveness of the "crime" of wishing a peer (brother) dead. It is an interesting theoretical possibility that the repression barrier was pierced and the ancient unconscious conflict around the brother sparked over into the preconscious. All the attendant psychological gain including energic shifts appeared to occur through the stimulation of the service of the Lord's Supper.

Perhaps as psychiatric research continues its investigations into the "conflict-free" (Hartmann) areas of the mind and into the processes that build healthy egos, a new appreciation of already existent means available to man, including his religion, for solving psychological conflict will ensue. The whole direction of this book is meant to emphasize the *total* resources offered by religion and the pastor's opportunities therein rather than the *relatively* insignificant resource of pastoral counseling. Our concept of pastoral care begs the clergyman to re-appreciate the potential of religious resources, besides counseling, to meet human needs.

The ideal pastor of the future, I believe, will not only be a skilled counselor, but he will also have an appreciation of the psychological power of religion in all its ramifications to modify and preserve the spirit of man. Because of his insight, he will be alerted to stresses, not commonly viewed as such, troubling his parishioners and will employ the already extant religious resources with a psychological understanding that enlarges and deepens their potency.

Since space prohibits a comprehensive categorization, we can only allude to a few of those superficially benign situations which, for some parishioners, carry deadly stresses. Common precipitants that bring patients for psychiatric help are: promotions and successes; pregnancies and birth; retirement; marriage of children, self, or parent; moves to a new city or new home; confirmations and Bar Mitzvahs; graduations; children leaving home; childlessness, especially at menopause; relatives into the home; a wife's working "successfully"; minor or near accidents; anniversaries of marriages, deaths, or major events; marriages mixed by religion or race; vasectomy and tubal ligation.

Although religious leaders have always emphasized the importance of the family, as their knowledge of psychological principles increases they will come into even more specific awareness of its effect on the growing child. They will have new appreciations of those conditions that give optimum chances to children to develop emotionally. Religious educators will pay increasing attention to psychological development and gear their educational methods and materials to the needs of the child and less to the teacher. I think pastors of the future, like physicians, will know the critical stages of development and how to assist parents constructively. They will know, for instance, that a child is *physiologically* incapable of being bowel or bladder trained until after eight or nine months; that the period from birth to a year in an infant's life is an especially critical one in the future mental health of the baby; that a child's play is also serious, important business in his development; that adolescence brings recrudescence of early developmental problems plus new ones; that impotence and frigidity are rarely, if ever, physical in origin but are rather allied with character and psychological conflict.

Some subtle stresses have been mentioned. However, through the ages the Church's wisdom has prepared in its ritual, sacrament, doctrine, literature, and pastoral care for those well-delineated moments of crisis in the life of man. It has provided to its adherents not only the succour but the inspiration and courage to remedy and work through trials of life. For example, in the *Book of Worship* of the Methodist Church (which has its counterpart in most denominations), its sections offer services of worship laden with materials designed to meet spiritual needs and holiday observances that capture not only religious tradition but human themes of life struggles. Its ritual addresses itself likewise to human needs and crises. Beginning with the service of holy communion it proceeds through the service of baptism, membership into the body of believers, marriage, burial of the dead, ordination, consecration, and dedication. Next in the *Book of Worship* comes a section on the ministry to the sick. All these rituals, services, and observances address themselves to psychological stress. Whether they accomplish this service by conscious intent or not is a side issue.

An analyst friend of mine told me that he had recently gotten more involved in his religion. He had found a small, integrated congregation wherein its members shared their lives in meaningful exchanges. He exemplified what he meant by finding religion's full potential in this group in the following episode: "In this congregation, if someone died, the relatives don't stay away. They come, red-eyed and in pain. One widowed woman, who had lost her husband that week, was so grief-stricken she couldn't eat the meal we always have after the service. An old man of the group came up to her, comforted her, and then began to feed her, like a baby. Seeing that reminded me somehow of the ancient Church and how it must have been—maybe that's why religion keeps on surviving."

In conclusion, it is my conviction that the psychological understanding of religion does not destroy religion but indeed may enhance its abilities to meet human needs. Religions will probably survive as long as man survives, provided they offer to and succeed in meeting his needs. Although there are theoretical, practical, and philosophical differences of great magnitude between religions and psychology, their common interest is man, his quirks, his assets and his needs. An enlightened religion will understand itself psychologically and bring its adherents the fruit of this understanding, not primarily in the special area of pastoral counseling, but in the whole of its pastoral care from sermon to sacrament, from pageantry to prayer, from belief to benediction.

INDEX